THE WIDER UNIVERSE

THE WIDER UNIVERSE

PAUL COUDERC
Astronome titulaire de l'Observatoire de Paris

ARROW SCIENCE SERIES

F09.2

ARROW BOOKS LTD

178-202 Great Portland Street, London, W.1

AN IMPRINT OF THE HUTCHINSON GROUP

London Melbourne Sydney
Auckland Bombay Toronto
Johannesburg New York

First Published in Great Britain 1960

Translated by
MARTIN DAVIDSON
from *L'Univers* first
published in France

*Made and printed in Great Britain
by Taylor Garnett Evans & Co. Ltd., Watford*

160304

CONTENTS

PLATES

PREFACE

The purpose of the author is to describe the distant regions of the Universe, about which our knowledge has advanced so remarkably during the last thirty years. No other science can boast of so much vitality. Even while the manuscript was being written, excellent new results have come to light which have gone to enrich the text. No astronomer can afford to keep out of touch with developments for any length of time without losing his grip.

Apart from describing the present known state of the Universe, some chapters contain speculations about the evolution of the stars and stellar systems. It is no longer possible to distinguish between *cosmology* and *cosmogony:* light rays reveal to us galaxies at different epochs, and no less than a thousand million years of evolution are unfolded before our eyes. The book concludes with a general view of the major problem of astronomy in our century—a problem which I have developed elsewhere.*

Following my usual method, I have not been afraid of repetition. The same fact may be treated in several chapters, but in different contexts or as seen from different angles. The reader must therefore not be surprised to discover slight numerical discrepancies in the results obtained by different methods.

It seems to me that no cultured person can afford to ignore the subject matter of this book. Not only does it provide a sketch of an ever-growing edifice that bears little resemblance to the notions of former generations, but it also brings the reader into close contact with the living developments of a scientific discipline—its facts, laws and attempts at interpretation. This, to my mind, is of great philosophic importance. Interpretations are modified whenever facts are consolidated, or when new data emerge. The gains are permanent; it would be foolish to deny all possibility of scientific certainty, just as it would be absurd to confer absolute value on current interpretations.

These essential truths are best illustrated by the successive editions of astronomical works.

Paul Couderc

*L'expansion de l'Univers. English translation by J. B. Sidgwick, *The Expansion of the Universe* (Faber, 1952).

1

General Considerations

Units of distance. The Earth is the largest of the solid bodies of which man is able to make use, and so its dimensions inevitably serve as a basis for the absolute measurement of astronomical distances. For our purpose it is sufficient to know that the Earth differs little from a sphere of radius 3,960 miles. In the planetary system the convenient unit of length is the mean distance (a) of the Sun from the Earth, the value of which is about 23,500 times the Earth's radius, but there is still an uncertainty of the order of one-thousandth in this value. We shall use the round number $a = 92,890,000$ miles.

The stars are too far away for this unit to be convenient. Astronomers use the *parsec**, but in this book we shall take as the unit *the light year* (abbreviation L.Y.) which is less technical and its significance is more easily remembered: it means the distance travelled by light in a year and is equal to about 6 million million miles. The parsec is equal to about 3·26 L.Y. and our actual investigations in the Universe take us at the moment as far as *a thousand million light years*.

Measurement of distances. The mathematical processes for the measurement of distances in astronomy are of the same nature as those in geodesy. The aim is to detect a change in direction of the object when

---

*A parsec is the distance from us at which the length a (the mean distance of the sun from the earth) subtends an angle of one second.

it is observed from two points separated as far as possible from each other. For instance, observations of a star are made at an interval of six months, from two opposite points of the Earth's orbit around the Sun. The *base* is then 186 million miles. This suffices for the detection of a slight change in the position of a nearby object with reference to much more distant stars, but this procedure loses all efficiency if the star being studied is not relatively very close, for the displacement to be measured rapidly becomes less than the errors of measurement on the photographic plates. The method does not give results of any value for stars further off than 500 L.Y.

Astronomy is indebted for all its information on greater distances, to a physical method—the *photometric* method—the principle of which is as follows:

Suppose we know the *absolute luminosity* of a star, that is, the amount of its energy output in kilowatts (for example, the Sun continuously emits 4.10^{23} kw)*. Let M be a conventional number, called *absolute magnitude*, which represents this amount. Let us now observe the *apparent* luminosity of this star —that is, the energy we receive on a normal screen at the Earth's surface. Let m be the number (*apparent magnitude*) which represents this luminosity in the conventional system of units used for M.

It is obvious that the comparison of m and M informs us about the distance of the star (on condition that space is transparent), for the apparent luminosity decreases in the ratio of the *square* of the

---

*Otherwise expressed, the total energy radiated per second by the Sun is $3 \cdot 8.10^{33}$ ergs, but only a very minute fraction of this falls on the surface of the Earth. An erg is equivalent to $7 \cdot 4.10^{-8}$ foot-pounds, and hence the total energy radiated per second by the Sun is about $2 \cdot 8.10^{26}$ foot-pounds, a force sufficient to raise ten million million million tons to a height of 10,000 feet!—*Translator's note.*

distance of the luminous source. In the usual system of magnitudes this difference (m—M), called the distance *modulus*, provides astronomers with the distance sought. Thus, a modulus equal to 5 corresponds to a distance of 326 L.Y., a modulus 10 to 3,260 L.Y., and so on.*

For this method to be meaningful it is necessary that we should know *a priori* the absolute luminosity of certain stars that are easy to identify at immense distances. Fortunately, the astronomer knows how to identify from their spectra certain *giant* stars (a hundred times more luminous than the Sun), and also certain *supergiants* (some ten thousand times more luminous than the Sun). These *standard* stars, which for the study of the heavens are the equivalent of buoys and lighthouses for navigation, make it possible to determine the distances of the clusters of stars to which they belong. It is then possible to calibrate the total luminosity of these clusters and make them serve as more powerful standard objects at distances where their component stars are indistinguishable and the clusters themselves appear as faint pale spots (or even as simple luminous points). Thus, astronomy has been able by this photometric method—so simple but requiring great care in application—to descend by steps into the abysses of space.

---

*The general formula, which involves the decimal logarithm, is

$$\log D = \frac{m - M}{5} + 1$$

if the distance D is expressed in parsecs. Or

$$\log D = \frac{m - M}{5} + 1\cdot51$$

if D is expressed in L.Y.

RADIAL VELOCITIES

Many of the essential data of astronomy involve radial velocities. It is important to understand fully what is meant by radial velocities and to grasp the method by which they are observed.

Fig. 1

The stars move along 'in space' relative to a given observer, and for the requirements of this small book it will be unnecessary to state this more precisely, but most readers will already be aware of the difficulties concealed in the words appearing in quotation marks. The *radial velocity* V_r of a star is the projection of its total velocity V on the line of sight OE (Fig. 1), and the study of a star's spectrum yields the radial velocity as an absolute value—for example, in kilometres per second. If the star is approaching us, the spectral lines are displaced towards the violet end of the spectrum. This may be observed by direct comparison with the spectrum of a reference source of light photographed through the same dispersive apparatus so as to appear adjacent to the spectrum of the star. If the star is receding, the displacement of the lines takes place towards the red end of the spectrum, for the wave-lengths are increased and the frequencies decreased. This phenomenon, known as the Doppler-Fizeau effect, obeys a simple law. The displacement $\Delta\lambda$ of a line of normal wave-length λ is such that

$$\frac{\Delta\lambda}{\lambda} = \frac{V_r}{c}$$

Expressed simply, we say that the *relative* displacement of the spectral lines is equal to the ratio of the star's radial velocity to the velocity of light (c).

Let us suppose that a star has a velocity equal to 186 miles/sec. in the direction of the observer, that is, a velocity equal to 1/1,000th that of light. All the spectral lines are then displaced towards the violet by one thousandth of their wave-length. Thus, the H_β line of hydrogen, which is situated at $\lambda = 4861 \cdot 35$ Å in the reference spectrum (the spectrum of a luminescent hydrogen tube, for example), appears in the star's spectrum (if it is there at all) displaced by $4 \cdot 86$Å and therefore opposite $\lambda = 4856 \cdot 49$ in the reference spectrum. The precision of the determination of a radial velocity obviously depends on the dispersion of the spectra used; under favourable conditions it can be accurate to less than one-third of a mile per second.

Our Galaxy. One of the great discoveries of astronomy is the form of the Galaxy, the visual appearance of which—as the 'Milky Way'—is a feebly luminous, irregular belt encircling the heavens like a girdle. Telescopes show a swarm of fine and crowded stars, which the naked eye is unable to distinguish. In the second half of the 18th century a few pioneers had the intuition that its appearance was not due to a thin band of stars but to a vast accumulation of considerable thickness. About 1800 it fell to the lot of William Herschel, an astronomer of genius, to point out by means of his 'gauges' the accuracy of these ideas. Herschel counted the stars, magnitude by magnitude, from the most brilliant to the faintest that he was able to see, in certain areas of the sky. While the bright stars visible to the naked eye were spread out rather uniformly on the celestial vault, the gauges showed that the faint stars became more numerous as the region that was studied approached closer to the Milky Way. There is a progressive concentration towards the Milky Way of stars that are fainter and therefore on the average more distant. We are thus led to conceive of an immense disk of thousands of millions of stars, a disk which we view from some point in its interior. In the directions of the plane of this disk the stars are seen accumulated in depth and form, as it were, a luminous barrier which is the Milky Way. Briefly, to us the Milky Way is like a disk seen edgewise from a point some distance within the circumference. The name *Galaxy* has been given to this immense, flattened agglomeration of stars, the profile of which is shown by the Milky Way (see Fig. 3).

In this Galaxy the Sun is an average star—average in luminosity and mass. If we look away from the plane of the Galaxy we see a relatively thin layer of stars; their images no longer touch and we see between them the dark background of the sky. The stars distinguishable to the naked eye are relatively near us and they occupy quite a small area around the Sun, small even compared to the thickness of the galactic disk in our neighbourhood. This is why we see them evenly distributed throughout the whole sky; the perspective of the galactic disk does not affect them. A study of the Galaxy will be made in Chapter 2, and it is sufficient to say here that the total mass of the Galaxy is about 200 thousand million times that of the Sun. The diameter of the galactic agglomeration is of the order of 80,000 light years, but its boundary is rather badly defined. There are, for example, 'deserters', or stars which are separated from the main population much as in the suburbs of a large town the houses gradually thin out until the countryside is reached. The boundaries of a town are conventional, and one has occasion to define a conventional boundary for the Galaxy in the same way.

In the Galaxy the Sun is a marginal star situated at about 30,000 L.Y. from the centre. In the solar regions the galactic disk is thin (perhaps 1,000 L.Y.), but at the centre of the Galaxy the stars are accumulated in a dense nucleus. This central bulge of the disk, which contains the main portion of the mass, has a thickness of 10,000 or perhaps 15,000 L.Y. The entire Galaxy turns like a wheel round this hub.*

The contents of the Universe. Out to the limits accessible to our investigation, we see the Universe occupied by *galaxies* similar to our own. These 'islands' of matter, each containing thousands of millions of stars but differing in form and size, stud the depths of space. Their relative independence lies in their spacing, and it is estimated that the average distance between the galaxies is equal to ten times the diamenter of the greatest of them. The giant telescope at Palomar Mountain is capable of photographing several thousands of millions of galaxies. This is a sample of the Universe worth considering, but can we take it as characteristic? Nothing in the examination (still superficial in our day) of the distant parts of the known domain gives grounds for suspecting any change whatever in the character of the population. It is, therefore, with a conviction of its homogeneity that cosmologists envisage the Universe as a whole.

In detail, however, what diversity! There are

*This does not imply that the angular velocities of the stars or clusters of stars are equal or nearly equal. As will be seen later, these differ very much. The word 'rotation' applied to the turning round of the Galaxy is not quite correct but is frequently used. The word 'revolution' which implies a motion similar to that of the orbital motions of the planets round the Sun would be a better description but would not always be correct. See page 37.

galaxies of *irregular* shapes; *ellipsoidal* galaxies every degree of flattening from the spheroid to the profile of a spindle; *spiral* galaxies resembling catherine wheels in every orientation and at every stage of unwinding. There are dwarf galaxies and giant galaxies; their relative luminosities can vary from 1 to 10,000, and this range can, perhaps, be still further extended because the dwarfs are not easy to discover.

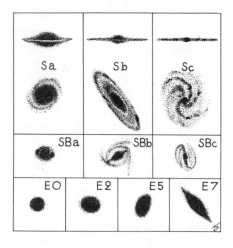

Fig. 2
The main types of spiral and elliptical galaxies (see p. 68).

Our Galaxy is a giant spiral and not at all exceptional. We know of many greater galaxies, starting with our neighbour, Messier 31 in Andromeda, the diameter of which seems to be double that of our Galaxy.

The galaxies show a strong tendency to be grouped. We often see them in twos, threes, fives or sixes, and sometimes come across groups of a score or more, like the *local cluster* to which our Galaxy and M* 31 both belong. Finally, photography of the heavens carried up to the 20th magnitude has recently re-

*M will be frequently used for Messier.

vealed the multitude of *giant clusters*, which group the galaxies by hundreds or even thousands. We know of more than a thousand of these great clusters, and we naturally wonder if there are any isolated galaxies, free between the clusters, or if the clusters may not finally touch one another with their less populated and greatly extended outlying parts. If this is so, we should be able to say that the Universe is populated with *clusters* of galaxies, rather than with galaxies, each cluster showing a very marked central agglomeration or 'nucleus' where the most massive galaxies have accumulated. Undoubtedly this is an extreme view; nevertheless, it seems probable that the galaxies associated in clusters are much more numerous than the 'outlaws', whether these latter are born in isolation as field galaxies or have escaped from the clusters by reason of great speed.

Cosmic material. Until 1930 it was believed that the space between the stars was empty; or rather, it was thought that the atoms or the particles which might occupy this space had no effect on our observations and represented only a very small percentage of the matter concentrated into stars. Since 1930 the proofs of the existence of interstellar matter have accumulated and the difficulties arising from its intervention in our galactic measurements are recognized. The galactic plane is packed with clouds of dusty gas. These clouds align themselves along the spiral arms of the Galaxy, which are traced out by them. The absorption of light, for which the fine dusts carrying the gas are almost entirely responsible, is specially strong in the direction of the galactic plane. This weakening of light is estimated to be, on the average, two magnitudes per kilo-parsec. This implies that after a journey of 3,000 years in the galactic plane, light has lost 84 per cent of its initial energy. At the end of 6,000 L.Y. there remains only 2·5 per cent of the original light; at the end of 9,000 L.Y. only 0·4 per cent of the photons remain and very little can be seen at all.

Like the stars, the clouds of gas are composed essentially of hydrogen; helium takes second place in them, but its atoms are only one twentieth the number of the hydrogen atoms. As for the other elements, their *total* mass undoubtedly does not attain 1 per cent of that of the two light gases. At present, the following mean composition by mass is attributed to the stars: hydrogen about 80 per cent, helium about 20 per cent, heavy elements less than 1 per cent. In other words, for every 10,000 atoms of hydrogen we find 500 atoms of helium and only 1 heavy atom. Our planet, the Earth, which has lost the main portion of its light gases (assuming that it initially had them) is not, therefore, a true sample of the universal matter.

Recent analysis of the primary cosmic ray particles confirms still further the supremacy of hydrogen. In these particles there has been found (by mass) 87 per cent of protons, 12 per cent of helium ions, and 1 per cent of heavy nuclei. If cosmic rays correctly describe interstellar matter, it may be remarked that the stars, like the Sun, have a little less hydrogen and a little more helium than cosmic gas, in so far as the present analyses allow us to judge. This result seems logical, because the stars derive their energy, light and heat by the transmutation of their hydrogen into helium. We should, therefore, find less hydrogen and more helium in the stars than in the cosmic gas from which they have probably been formed, and this would be a striking indication of evolution. By comparing the proportions of the hydrogen-helium mixture in space and in the stars, we may even hope to estimate for how long a star of known energy output must have been carrying out the observed transmutation by emitting radiation.

But the transmutation takes place in the deep regions of the stars, and most astronomers are convinced that such variation of the chemical composition would not be apparent in their atmospheres (which we can analyse) in the absence of an efficient mixing of the stellar matter. The chemical composition would vary with the depth but would remain invariable on the surface, at least for normal stars, which are sufficiently quiescent and have a moderate rotation.

The slight difference in composition ascertained between cosmic gas and stars, if it is confirmed, could be explained in many ways, beginning with the primary conditions for the formation of stars. However, we are still very uncertain about these conditions and shall not pursue the question further here.

Absorbing dust. Just as the air that we breathe carries dust, so cosmic gas carries solid particles, the total mass of which appears to be one-fiftieth that of the gas. (It seems probable that these particles, in the course of time, originate and increase in the gas, as a result of collisions between the atoms or between particles and atoms.) But the solid particles have an enormous power of scattering or absorbing—and consequently of obstructing—the light, and to them is attributed the essential role in absorption in the Galaxy. The diameter of the effective absorbing particles is of the order of $0 \cdot 1 \mu$. A cosmic cloud having 10 atoms of hydrogen per cubic centimetre will perhaps carry one particle of dust per cubic hectometre.

The energy of the stars. The stars are atomic reactors, and in most cases they have been in constant operation for a long time. Thermonuclear reactions are induced and continue in the deep regions where the temperature stands at from 10 to 20 million degrees absolute. These reactions start when the temperature is high enough to excite the atomic nuclei to such speeds that their intercollisions provide sufficient energy to enable them to overcome their natural repulsions and unite. (These repulsions are called 'Coulomb forces' and are due to the fact that their electric charges are all of the same sign— namely, positive.)

Essentially there are two possible cycles of nuclear reactions that occur. The simplest cycle, called the proton-proton, or (P,P), cycle, prevails at the lowest interior temperatures. It is similar to the reactions which take place in the hydrogen bomb, and the circumstances of this are given in Appendix I. The output of energy increases in the ratio of the fourth power of the absolute temperature (T^4). The other reaction cycle is known as the carbon or carbon-nitrogen (C,N) cycle. It is also called the Bethe cycle, in honour of H. Bethe who first worked out its details in 1939. We may remark that Bethe's cycle preceded by seven years the explosion of the first atomic bomb, and also that it is prior in conception to the proton-proton cycle; physicists were not sure of the first and third reactions in the (P,P) cycle until 1951 (Cf. Appendix I).

The (C,N) cycle utilises the carbon and nitrogen as simple catalysts and the final result is the conversion of hydrogen into helium. For its initiation or 'priming' the (C,N) cycle involves higher temperatures than the (P,P) cycle, but once it is in operation it predominates over the latter because its yield is proportional to a very high power of the temperature (T^{21}).*

To summarise, the hot stars radiate by the process of the Bethe cycle, while the cooler stars depend on the proton-proton cycle. The Sun is close to the conditions where the two cycles exchange their predominance; from 1938 to 1953 credit was given in the Sun to the Bethe cycle only, but more refined calculations, based on better data from the laboratory, now show that the (P,P) cycle provides at least 99 per cent of its energy. The demarcation occurs for stars of spectral type a little hotter than the Sun. The central temperature of the Sun appears to be a little less than 14 million degrees.

THE AGE OF THE EARTH

The Earth's age plays a very important role in cosmology because it provides a minimum of duration for the Universe. Every cosmological theory which is unable to account for the existence of the Universe for a period in the past *at least equal to* the Earth's age, would naturally be condemned. Indeed, any valid theory should lead to durations much greater than the Earth's age, for we can hardly imagine that our small solid globe, placed as it is in a well-organised system of galaxies and clusters of galaxies, was contemporaneous with the first developments of these immense, imbricated structures. Rather, we conceive a process of evolution proceeding from the more general to the particular, carving up the great material blocks of the Universe, dividing and subdividing them until, at last, the residues left over

*Absolute temperature will be assumed in the future unless otherwise stated.

from the important operations are organised in the lowest domain.

Be this as it may, the age of the Earth is a precise and invaluable fixed point embedded in our tentative and uncertain evaluations of the time scale. By the 'age' of the Earth we actually mean the age of the terrestrial crust—or, more precisely, the time which has elapsed since the first solid continents floated on the magma of the original globe.

Geologists do not think that a very long time can have elapsed between the original appearance of the Earth as an isolated body, composed of the mass of materials with which we are acquainted, and the appearance of the first continents. We can compare the earliest processes to the rapid formation of layers of scoria on the surface of a crucible of melted ore as soon as one ceases to heat it. Whatever may have been the mechanism of the agglomeration of terrestrial materials, it could not have taken place without the liberation of sufficient heat to melt them—indeed, they may have been molten, or even volatile, at the very outset.

Without great effort of the imagination or serious risk of error we may, then, consider the fused terrestrial mass as very rapidly losing its superficial heat into space. Solid islets are formed by the cooling at the surface when the temperature falls below 1,500°; the lightest minerals (of density less than 3), which will later form the terrestial rocks, then begin to appear*. In time, an insulating and continuous crust is formed, under the protection of which the main

*This light mineral matter is a skin of silicates of aluminium (*Sial*) about 30 miles thick, floating on a deep bed of silicates of magnesium (*Sima*) perhaps 2,000 miles thick, surrounding the liquid core of the Earth.

internal mass of materials can maintain its heat and its liquid properties.

This solid crust will certainly undergo innumerable changes during the course of the thousands of millions of years that elapse until the appearance of man, and it is extremely improbable that we should be able to find in it any original fragment remaining undamaged through all the major modifications. Nevertheless, science believes that it is capable of assigning a definite age to this initial crust, in one operation involving several stages.

1. *The Age of the Oldest known Minerals*. Lead, a common metal, is a mixture of four *isotopes* of atomic masses 204, 206, 207 and 208, the percentages of which in normal lead are $1 \cdot 36$, $25 \cdot 3$, $21 \cdot 2$ and $52 \cdot 1$. Lead 204 is not generated at all in the terrestial crust; it is not the product of any known natural radioactivity and has been in the crust since it was formed, though it may have been the product of a rapid radio-activity accomplished before the appearance of the Earth. But the other three isotopes have emananted from known radio-activities which still continue; lead 206 is derived from uranium 238, lead 207 from uranium 235, lead 208 from thorium 232. We know the speeds of these three radio-active processes—speeds that are rigorously constant—and we have proof that they have not varied in the course of the ages. They constitute independent time-keepers which measure the ages of the minerals analysed. A sample of granite, for example, contains uranium, and an analysis reveals its present content of uranium 238 and 235, and of lead 206 and 207. The *lead ratios* Pb 206/U 238 and Pb 207/U 235 are characteristics of the age of the mineral, for they have evolved (and still evolve) in the course of time and they make it possible

to specify the epoch in which the specimen was deposited.

Naturally, it is desirable to take into consideration the quantity of lead 206 and 207 which the mineral could have contained at the moment when it was deposited, before its own local and relatively undisturbed radioactivities may be said to have begun. In a given sample the lead 204 content is trustworthy evidence of the amounts of *common* lead which can be relegated to the earlier age, since lead 204 remains constant. It is therefore sufficient to know the isotopic composition of ordinary lead at different epochs of the past to be able to deduce the amounts of secondary lead. We shall see that still greater importance is attached to isotopic analysis of the *galenas* (mineral sulphides of lead) of all geological ages. In addition, as we are concerned with *ancient* rocks—for these are of the greatest interest here—the quantities of secondary lead so far outweigh the traces of the original lead that the latter can be neglected on first approximation. Later, it may be used for improving the evaluations. What, then, are the results of the analysis of samples taken from the oldest known rocks in all parts of the world?

In America, the record for antiquity is held by the *pegmatites* of the south-east of Manitoba, the age of which is 2·4 thousand million years. In Africa, the pegmatites of Southern Rhodesia (Bikita) have indicated 2·65 thousand million years (Alfred Nier, 1954).

An associated result proves still more instructive: the pegmatites of Rhodesia are taken from a layer of alluvial deposits obviously more ancient still (the Bulawayan system) and in the graptolite limestones associated with this level some structures indicating the presence of *algae* were discovered in 1953. Hence, not only has the terrestrial crust existed for at least 2·7 thousand million years, but life then showed itself already in complex forms. The conditions of temperature were therefore similar to those that we know now, and hence we can deduce that *solar radiation has been practically constant for at least three thousand million years*. The period available for the evolution of living species now seems to be much longer than was formerly believed. More recently still, workers at the University of Toronto laboratory of Geophysics have published a list of forty-five ancient minerals from Africa, dated by their radio-activities or by their isotopic composition. The ages of the oldest specimens in thousands of millions of years are as follows:

Galena from Bondo (Belgian Congo) 2·79 $\pm$ 0·09
Galena from Barberton (South Africa) 2·86 $\pm$ 0·06
Monazite from Sierra Leone   2·93 $\pm$ 0·20

At the end of 1954 the latest sample held the world's record, coming very close to three thousand million years. The indicated degrees of possible error show that these results can be trusted to within about 5 per cent. The agreement with the researches of other laboratories, and the unbroken series of ages covering from a thousand million to three thousand million years, show that this is not an isolated result about which there might be some doubt.

The oldest specimens come from the continental insular shelf, regarded for a long time as primordial, and it may be considered that here we reach the nuclei of the condensations formed at that time when the Earth's interior was hotter than it has been since the more recent solidifications. The structure and the composition of these continental nuclei differ from those of later beds.

2. *The Upper Limit to the age of the Earth's Crust.* Let us imagine that all the lead 207 now found in the rocks was produced at the expense of uranium 235 after the crust was formed; by thus discounting any original lead 207, we obtain a very high proportion of secondary lead. This lead ratio thus implies an age that is too great. The best established evaluations made in this way give 5·4 thousand million years. Thus, we have determined the age of the crust to between two limits, the minimum and maximum differing only by a factor less than 2. In thousands of millions of years:

$$2 \cdot 9 < \text{age of the crust} < 5 \cdot 4$$

But we shall now show how a more precise value within these limits may be obtained.

3. *The Age of the Earth's Crust deduced from Lead Minerals.* Let T be the age of the crust and 1, x and y the relative amounts of the isotopes 204, 206 and 207 in the original lead: T, x and y are three unknowns. Lead 204, which remains unchanged in the course of time, is taken as a unit of reference for measuring the amounts of the isotopes 206 and 207, which will vary in the course of time as a function of the known speed of radio-activity and of the quantities of uranium present in the terrestial region studied.

The lead minerals that we discover in the formations of various well-known geological ages, afford evidence of the steady enrichment of the original lead. In fact, the Pre-Cambrian, Primary, Secondary and Tertiary rocks have compositions which imply an evolution conforming with the preceding ideas. Sir Arthur Holmes showed in 1946 how a collection of galenas of different ages makes it possible to determine the three unknowns T, x and y. The principle of this method is simple, and we give the details of it in Appendix II, the interesting feature being the elimination of the erratic *local* amounts of uranium, which play no part in the solution.

Holmes's results, which are of excellent quality, are based on only thirty galenas analysed with the greatest care. More recently, a method of speedy analysis has been applied in Toronto to several hundreds of specimens. The results are:

$T = 3 \cdot 5$ thousand million years. $x = 11 \cdot 0$, $y = 13 \cdot 5$

At the present time we have, in proportion to Pb 204 in ordinary lead, Pb 206 $= 18 \cdot 7$, Pb 207 $= 15 \cdot 6$.

The value of T above is, moreover, a *minimum*, for it implies the hypothesis that the addition of isotopes has been continuous since the epoch T. Geologists do not attribute to the terrestrial surface—especially in its early stages—such stability that setbacks (in particular, local ones) have not been possible. Such processes, delaying the start of the enrichment in isotopes, could not but impair the mean value of T which we deduced from the collection of minerals. Nevertheless, three analysed specimens suffice to calculate the three unknowns, and hundreds of galenas, from all parts of the globe, taken in threes, lend themselves to the determination of these quantities. Setting aside some abnormal specimens, the majority of the solutions, taken on the whole, agree to within about 10 per cent.

To sum up, the definitive terrestrial crust was formed about $3 \cdot 5$ thousand million years ago, and it seems that the age of the Earth, in so far as it is a celestial body, cannot be much less than 4,000 million years.

2

Our Galaxy

The Milky Way. The Milky Way is a whitish irregular band which spans the heavens, following approximately a great circle. Since its observation through a telescope by Galileo in 1610, we know that this appearance is due to the accumulation of a considerable number of stars along this belt. As we turn our gaze from the Milky Way to a direction perpendicular to its plane, that is, towards its poles, we observe through the telescope a progressively decreasing number of stars.

Since the middle of the 18th century, a certain number of philosophers (amongst them Emmanuel Kant) and other enquirers understood that the Milky Way was the appearance of a gigantic stellar system in which the Sun was immersed. They realised that it was not a belt without thickness, but an accumulation of enormous depth. This flat, disc-shaped system of stars, of which the Sun is part, was given the name of the *Galaxy*. The Milky Way is a section of it seen from a point inside the agglomeration. In directions at a sufficiently large angle from the plane of the Milky Way, the observer sees a thin layer of stars, all relatively near the Sun, and they appear far enough apart for the dark background of the sky to predominate. But when we look into the Milky Way itself, the thick mass of tiny light-points sometimes seems to completely obliterate the background of the sky. In fact, observations in the Milky

Way are often materially impeded by the effects of absorption; light is scattered by the clouds of dust—that is, by solid particles of very small diameter (of the order of $0 \cdot 1\mu$) which carry the layers of inter-stellar gas.

THE GALAXY AND STAR COUNTS

The first astronomer who tried to establish the structure of the Galaxy by stellar statistics was William Herschel. His celebrated 'gauges', prepared over a period of years around 1800, were obtained by counting the stars, magnitude by magnitude, in certain areas of the heavens, up to the limit of visibility of his telescope (18 ins. aperture, limiting magnitude about 14). He thus explored 3,400 areas well distributed over the whole accessible part of the sky, and his son John continued his work by carefully examining, at the Cape, 1800 areas of the southern sky.

	Number of Stars per Unit Area			Galactic Concentration L/H
	L	M	H	
Up to m_{pg} = 8	8	5	3	$2 \cdot 7$
= 12	430	230	138	$3 \cdot 1$
= 16	15,000	6,000	2,700	$5 \cdot 5$
= 20	280,000	64,000	21,000	$13 \cdot 3$

L = Low latitudes ($< 20°$)   H = High latitudes ($> 40°$)
M = Middle latitudes m_{pg} = Photographic magnitude

William Herschel demonstrated the phenomenon of *galactic concentration*. The stars invisible to the naked eye are the more numerous in a square degree of the sky as the galactic latitude of the square is lower; the fainter the stars studied, the more striking is this increase. The (modern) Table above, where the sky is simply divided into three equal zones, shows the relative numbers of stars brighter than the magnitude indicated on the left, and indicates and extends Herschel's results.

Herschel also recognised that, for a given magnitude, the star density depends practically only on the galactic latitude; the fluctuations in longitude seemed to him to be very small. In the region reached by his telescope, everything appeared as though the Sun were situated in the vicinity of the centre of the agglomeration. Here we may mention that this illusion persisted up to 1918 (as long as counting remained the chief source of information) and we shall now see why this was so.

The 20th Century Censuses. During the first two decades of this century the deeper censuses which, so to speak, extended Herschel's gauges, were based on a much greater wealth of records provided by the use of photography, the *Carte du Ciel*, and large improved telescopes. This was the period in which Kapteyn, and his famous computing laboratory at Groningen (Holland), showed what can be achieved by the centralization of records and by their intensive exploitation.

The results were excellent in the sphere of kinematics and showed in particular the peculiar dissymmetries in the motions of the stars in our neighbourhood. These peculiarities did not find a satisfactory explanation till after the discovery of the structure of the Galaxy, and this discovery did not by any means result from the statistics. Indeed, statistics persisted in suggesting the view that the density of the stars in space decreased regularly in all directions around the Sun, as though the Sun belonged to a region of maximum density. The truth, as we shall soon see, is almost the opposite; we belong to a region that is poor in stars.

The principal cause of the statistical failure is the presence in the interstellar 'void' of absorbing matter, the existence of which we have mentioned, and which is irregularly distributed. The absorption alters the brightness of the stars, makes them seem dimmer and further off than they are, especially when their light passes by chance through a particularly dense nebulosity. The apparent diminution of the number of stars in all directions is merely an effect of the haze. The powerful effects of absorption have been fully recognised, estimated and corrected only since 1930. Owing to bad luck the haze is particularly opaque in the most interesting directions, such as that of the centre of the Galaxy.

Statistics which indiscriminately include all categories of stars have, in addition, another serious defect: they do not take into consideration the extraordinary intrinsic variety of stellar luminosities. There are dwarf stars a million times less luminous than the Sun and super-giants which radiate a million times more than the Sun. Any star whatever, of a given apparent magnitude can, if we have no other information about it, be just as well a very close dwarf as a very distant supergiant. Censuses based without selection on the apparent magnitude only, are fundamentally marred by this immense range of absolute luminosities. Further, there was never any agreement about the relative *frequency* in space of the stars with different luminous powers (the *luminosity function*). The recent recognition of several types of stellar populations—at least two—increases the complexity of the question, especially if the types are mixed, as happens in our vicinity. Certainly the supergiants are rare, but are the extreme dwarfs (which the eye misses when they are not very near) really more numerous, as is believed, or are they also rare? This matter is still in dispute.

We see the reasons for the weakness of too general statistics. To penetrate far into the Universe it is necessary to select the objects and to concentrate on those which have the maximum intrinsic brightness. It is a fact that the most skilful and the most conscientious star counts have not disclosed the organization of the Galaxy, the order of its size, or the position in it that the Sun occupies. We shall now describe how this vital information has been ascertained.

THE GLOBULAR CLUSTERS AND THE CENTRE OF THE GALAXY

For a long time we have known of a hundred almost spherical or 'globular' clusters in which the stars are very strongly concentrated towards the centre. In photographs, the images of the stars overlap in the middle of the cluster, and it is impossible to count them except beyond a certain distance from the centre. In several clusters some five thousand peripheral stars have been thus counted. Furthermore, these clusters are all very far away and the only stars which are counted are the *giants*; the dwarfs are more numerous. The mass of such a cluster is of the order 10^6 Suns (a million times that of the Sun). But the Galaxy is a stellar formation of quite another order of size; the stars in it are reckoned by *thousands of millions* (we shall see that we may go even up to hundreds of thousands of millions). There is, then, no doubt that the galactic globular clusters are controlled by the powerful gravitation of the Galaxy and they do, in fact, revolve around its centre just as the

Earth revolves around the Sun. A statistical proof of the dependence of the globular clusters on the Galaxy lies in the fact that there are as many north as south of the Milky Way: in other words, the galactic plane is a *plane of symmetry* for the system formed by the hundred globular clusters. But the globular clusters are curiously distributed in the vault of the sky; they

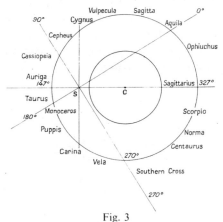

Fig. 3
Plan of the Milky Way
From the Sun S, the constellations lying along the Milky Way are seen in the order shown. The numbers indicate some galactic longitudes. The centre of the Galaxy C is seen from S in the direction of longitude 327° (in Sagittarius).

are concentrated at one side of the constellation *Sagittarius*. About thirty are found in the immediate vicinity of this constellation, and the others are found (with only a few exceptions) on the celestial hemisphere of which Sagittarius would be the pole. In other words, looked at from the Sun, we see almost all the clusters in the same direction, in the neighbourhood of Sagittarius.

Conclusion. The centre of the Galaxy, round which the clusters revolve, must be situated in the direction of Sagittarius. It is also very far away from the Sun because we must be on the edge of the system of clusters in order to see almost all of them towards the Galactic centre. (See Figs. 3, 4 and 5). The astronomer, Shapley, in suggesting this conclusion in 1918, added to it some numerical values. For that purpose he had determined at Mount Wilson the distances of the globular clusters by new methods which were to prove very useful in the future, and which we shall now consider.

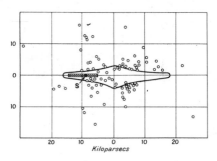

Fig. 4
Sketch of the Galactic System
Distribution of the main globular clusters around the galactic disk (1 kiloparsec = 3260 light years). The shaded area containing the Sun represents the region accessible to ordinary investigation.

The RR Lyrae Stars. The RR Lyrae type stars are white, variable, *giants*. Their luminosities are approximately equal to a *hundred* times that of the Sun, but they undergo rapid periodic fluctuations. The periods are of the order of 12 hours (less than a day in all cases). The behaviour of the light variation is characteristic. After a fairly sudden flare there follows a

Above: Great Nebula in Orion, M 42. (100-inch telescope.)
Below: Filamentous Nebula in Cygnus, NGC 6992. (60-inch telescope.)

[*Palomar*]

Above: Supernova in IC 4182; A, maximum brightness, Aug. 23, 1937 (exposure 20 mins.); B, very faint, Nov. 4, 1938 (exposure 45 mins.); C, invisible, Jan. 19, 1942 (exposure 85 mins.). The nebulosity brought out by the increased photographic exposure is not a product of the supernova. *Below:* Globular Cluster in Hercules, NGC 6205 (M 13). (200-inch telescope.)

slower lapse to the initial brightness. Shapley was able to identify RR Lyrae stars in a certain number of clusters and to determine their distances by the photometric method (see Chapter 1), since the absolute magnitude of these standard stars is known. ($M=0$, almost exactly.) This enabled him to calibrate the stars of maximum luminosity found in the

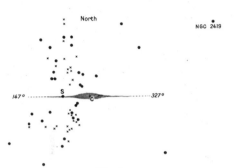

Fig. 5

Section of our Galaxy

Projection of the best known globular clusters (.), and of distant high-velocity stars that have been specially studied (x), on to a plane perpendicular to the galactic plane and passing through SC (Sun and Galactic Centre).

clusters (that is, the red supergiants), and to make them serve, in their turn, as standard stars to find the distances of clusters farther away.

Finally, in the poorly resolved clusters (i.e., the most distant) Shapley utilised the total luminosity of the cluster, as deduced from its type, for the classification of clusters of known distance had revealed the existence of a small number of typical varieties of clusters. In fact, Shapley was able to list the distances of sixty clusters, and then establish their real distribution in space. The figure obtained is characteristic (Figs. 4 and 5). Some corrections had subsequently to be made to the dimensions suggested by Shapley, after the discovery of interstellar absorption, but his general results obtained have remained valid.

1. The centre of the Galaxy is situated in the direction of Sagittarius, at galactic longitude 327°.

2. The Sun's distance from this centre is about 27,000 L.Y.

3. The Galaxy extends in its principal plane for, perhaps, 100,000 L.Y.

4. The collection of globular clusters forms a spheroidal system concentric with the Galaxy. In other words, our globular clusters people a sphere centred on the galactic nucleus, a sphere of at least 150,000 L.Y. in diameter.

Now that these results are known, it is clear that the centre of the Galaxy might have been ascertained long since from the appearances alone. Not only is the Milky Way in Sagittarius specially plentiful in stars, clustered together, but in this region also are to be found those distant and singular objects, the globular clusters, the Novae, the bright and dark nebulae, the free RR Lyrae stars (not inside the globular clusters), and those stars with very extensive atmospheres inappropriately called *planetary nebulae.*

Baade's RR Lyrae Stars (1950). Baade discovered that the nuclei of galaxies are composed of a stellar population called Population II, the brightest stars of which are red. Furthermore, these nuclei are concealed behind a dense haze through which only the red rays can penetrate in an appreciable quantity. To reveal the nucleus of our Galaxy, Baade therefore analysed a series of negatives of Sagittarius taken in red light with the 100-inch telescope at Mount Wilson. He counted more than 1,000 stars per square degree, most of them of the RR Lyrae type; their accumulation is striking up to apparent magnitude $m = 17 \cdot 5$ (Fig. 6). An absorption in this direction of $\Delta m = 2 \cdot 8$ magnitudes was determined from studies of the reddening of the light, so that we should take for the corrected magnitude, $m = 17 \cdot 5 - 2 \cdot 8 = 14 \cdot 7$. As these stars have an absolute magnitude $M = 0$, their distance modulus, $m - M$, is also $14 \cdot 7$, which corresponds to a distance of 28,000 L.Y.

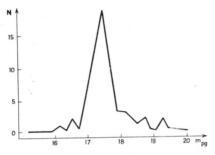

Fig. 6
Classification of the short-period
variables in Sagittarius
Abscissae: Apparent photographic magnitudes m_{pg}.
Ordinates: Relative number N of variables observed at each magnitude.

'KINEMATIC' DETERMINATIONS

The vertex. In 1904 Kapteyn showed that even if we allow for the effect of the Sun's own motion towards a point (the apex) not far from Vega, the motions of the stars in space are far from random; they form two streams moving in two particular directions. K. Schwarzschild proposed a successful interpretation of these streams. The velocity vectors of the stars are greater in a certain direction in space than in any other. This preferential direction is in the *plane of the Milky Way*, and on one side it is approximately towards longitude 325° (*the vertex*). It will already be seen that the vertex is no other than the centre of the Galaxy described by Shapley, and its significance is clear: the stars have individual speeds influenced by the powerful attraction of the galactic nucleus, and they have a greater mobility in the direction of this nucleus.

Kapteyn's two streams were only a particular aspect of this phenomenon, due to a somewhat special grouping of the data. To obtain two streams analogous to those proposed by Kapteyn, it is sufficient to group on the one hand the stars that are moving towards the celestial hemisphere of which the vertex would be a pole, and on the other hand those which show a preference for the opposite direction. The two streams then run in contrary senses, along the direction of the vertex.

The asymmetric current. Another complication arose later when attention was drawn to the high-velocity stars or to more distant objects. By 'high-velocity stars' we mean those whose speeds (allowing for the motion of the Sun towards the vertex) exceed 75 km./sec. Such velocities are all directed towards the celestial hemisphere whose pole would be the point in the Milky Way at longitude 235°. Similarly, the globular clusters, taken in their totality, show a very high preferential velocity (about 200 km./sec.) in the same direction.

This is the direction of what has been called the *asymmetric current*, the significance of which remained puzzling until the discovery of the galactic rotation, which solved the problem. No doubt it will have been observed that the direction of this stream is perpendicular to that of the vertex. In other words, the asymmetric current points about 90° from the galactic centre (325° = 235° + 90°).

Rotation of the Galaxy. The very flat shape of the Galaxy makes it extremely probable that it has a general rotation round an axis perpendicular to its plane. Then again, since 1924, its similarity to the family of spiral nebulae has been recognised, and the spectrograph shows us that the spirals rotate (Doppler-Fizeau effect).

If the law of the rotation of the stars around the centre is similar to that of the planets around the Sun, it should be possible to detect the differences of speed between stars placed at unequal distances from the centre. For the planets, the period P of revolution increases with the distance from the Sun according to Kepler's third law (P^2/a^3 = a constant), and the speed of revolution on the orbit decreases with the distance according to the formula $V^2 :: 1/a$*.

If the stars obey analogous laws (a hypothesis which the preponderating mass of the galactic nucleus renders probable), the stars nearer the centre than the Sun move more quickly than the latter and the stars more distant than the Sun move slower. *With reference to the Sun*, stars sufficiently distant should show systematic velocities such as are indicated in Fig. 7. This kinematic dissymmetry between the four quadrants of the galactic plane should be sufficient to show—especially by means of the radial velocities (Fig. 7, diagram 3)—the differential rotation.

Lindblad's theoretical developments, and after-

---

*A more accurate way of expressing this is $V^2 :: (2/r — 1/a)$, where r is the distance of the planet from the Sun and a is the semi-axis major of the ellipse described by the planet round the Sun. As r and a do not differ very much for most of the planets, the formula given is sufficiently accurate for approximations.—*Translator's Note.*

wards the method proposed by Oort in 1927, have made it possible since 1928 to show that this differential rotation does take place. Observations fully confirm the theory and furnish the following results:

1. The direction of the centre: longitude 327°.

2. Distance of the Sun from the centre: 27,000 L.Y.

3. Speed of the Sun: 220 km./sec. in the direction of longitude 57°. The Sun accomplishes its revolution in 250 million years (the cosmic year).

4. The variation of angular velocity of the motion in the neighbourhood of the Sun is such that the stars situated radially in the Galaxy at a distance of 3,000 L.Y. from the Sun, describe *one* radian more or less than the Sun in 200 million years.

Fig. 7

Differential Rotation

Stars A and B, which are nearer the Galactic Centre, have higher orbital velocities than the Sun S. Stars C and D, which are further away, go round more slowly than the Sun. The second diagram shows the differences of these velocities relative to S (supposed fixed). The last diagram shows the unsymmetrical radial velocities of A, B, C, D which result from this.

In other words, the displacement and mixing are rapid in the interior of the Galaxy. In a thousand million years the Sun performs four circuits; a cluster 3,000 L.Y. from the Sun, and towards the galactic centre, performs five circuits, and a cluster at a distance of 30,000 L.Y. from the centre accomplishes only three circuits (approximately). But we shall see that this law of revolution about the galactic centre varies in the central region itself.

Further reflections on the asymmetric current (*towards* 235°). The fast stars and the globular clusters appear, then, to be moving to the point opposite to 57°, towards which the Sun is carried by the rotation. The order of magnitude of the relative speed of the system of globular clusters with reference to the Sun shows that this system practically takes no part in the galactic rotation. As for the stars called '*fast*', these are really stragglers that the Sun overtakes and leaves behind. Their speed in the galactic rotation is less than $220 - 75 = 145$ km./sec., and here we have the explanation of why 'forward' speeds greater than 75 km./sec. with reference to the Sun are not observed. For the so-called *parabolic* speed (the 'escape velocity'), which is sufficient to detach a satellite from its central body and to carry it off to infinity, differs from the speed on a circular orbit by a factor of only $\sqrt{2}$, and here it approaches 300 km./sec. Every star in the neighbourhood of the Sun which would have a speed of 75 km./sec. in addition to that of the Sun (that is, directed towards $l = 57°$) would obviously have the parabolic speed and would move away from the Galaxy altogether. The solar orbit has, therefore, been freed from such stars long since.

ROTATION OF THE GALAXY AT DIFFERENT DISTANCES FROM THE CENTRE

The preceding results showed, between 1925 and 1930, that our Sun occupies a galactic region where the speed of rotation decreases with the distance from the centre. Is this law valid all along the radius? Observation suggests that it is not so in the neighbouring galaxies, especially in M 31, and Mayall showed in 1950 (see Chapter 4, p. 82) that the speed, starting from the nucleus, actually increases at first, passes through a maximum, and then decreases. Evidence of the same phenomenon in the Galaxy was sought and immediately found in the radial velocities of the far off Cepheids. The Cepheids closest to the nucleus have smaller velocities in their circulation than those near the Sun, and a maximum speed has been found at 5,000 L.Y. from the Sun, in a direction towards the centre.

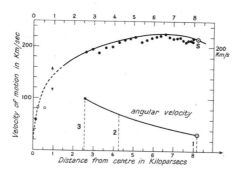

Fig. 8

Orbital velocities in the Galaxy at various distances from the centre, and the corresponding angular velocities of revolution (that of the Sun ☉ being taken as unity).

This result was fully confirmed and definitely established at the end of 1954 by the Dutch group of radio-astronomers. The study of neutral hydrogen on wave-length 21 cm. provided very accurate determinations, and Fig. 8 shows the speeds of rotation at different distances from the centre. (The dotted portion is less certain.) The graduation of the scale of abscissae is in kiloparsecs (3,260 L.Y.), and the Sun is represented by ☉; its speed is about 216 km./sec. The maximum occurs at 6·5 kiloparsecs from the centre and does not exceed 226 km./sec. The height of the continuous curve represents the variation of the speed of circulation in the Galaxy, and the dots represent *measured* values. But, in accordance with the procedure employed, the measured speed between the spiral arms is a little less than the speed of rotation. When the point is *on* the curve it marks the site of an arm. The figure accordingly shows the arms at 3, at 5 and at 6·6 kps. from the centre. Further, the Sun at 8·2 kps. from the centre is near another arm (Cf. Fig. 9).

Absorption in the Galaxy. The proofs of the existence of diffuse materials (gas and dust clouds) in the Galaxy have increased since 1930. For a long time bright or dark diffuse nebulosities, opaque screens, and areas denuded of distant stars, have been observed in the Milky Way. Indications of absorption on apparently clear paths are no longer wanting (absorption lines, called *interstellar*, caused by interstellar gas, and the reddening of distant objects). We have been obliged for a long time to admit the general presence of interstellar material and the great extent of its effects.

Since we know that the galaxies—spiral or otherwise—are objects situated outside the limits of our own Galaxy, counts of these objects are characteristic: they are never found in low latitudes. The zone comprised between latitudes ± 20° is, for this reason, called the *Zone of Avoidance*. It shows that a layer of absorbing matter extends through the whole galactic plane. This flattened layer impedes but little the observations towards the higher latitudes but stops the light rays which travel through the haze in the directions of low latitude. The haze is not penetrated except in latitudes greater than 20°, save in exceptional cases ('windows'). In the direction of the galactic centre, where the dust is more dense and the layer thicker, the absorption is greater than in the opposite direction.

The powerful effect of absorption was shown in 1930 by Trumpler: he studied the star clusters which are observed in the Milky Way—so-called *open* clusters (only slightly condensed), as opposed to the very congested globular clusters. Several hundreds of these are known, situated at various distances up to 10 to 15 thousand L.Y. Having selected similar clusters (by the number and nature of their stars and their degree of concentration), and determined their distances by the photometric method, Trumpler expected to find in them linear diameters of the same order of size. (The distance and the *apparent* diameter give the true diameter.)

To his great surprise the diameter *increased* with the distance from the Sun. This unacceptable result showed the existence of a systematic error in the distances, which had been overestimated. Trumpler therefore attributed the blame to a separate absorption which, diminishing the light of his distance indicators, made them appear more distant than they actually were. To restore the distant clusters to the order of size of those that were nearer, Trumpler saw that it was necessary to infer *one magnitude* of absorption per 4,000 L.Y. of travel in the Galaxy. It is estimated to-day that an absorption *twice* this amount (two magnitudes per 4,000 L.Y.) is pretty frequent, yet it represents only an average: there are *clear* directions and very *hazy* directions, and in the direction of the centre of the Galaxy a very much heavier absorption should be envisaged. It would be an enormous work merely to compile absorption charts for the various directions of the Milky Way, deduced from stellar reddening and extinction.

The reddening proves that the radiations of long wave length (λ) are less absorbed than the short radiations (ultra-violet, violet or blue). The degree of scattering seems to be proportional to $1/\lambda$ and this law suggests as affective absorbers particles of the order of $0 \cdot 1\mu$ (called 'dust'). $1\mu = 1$ micron $= 0.0001$ cm.

In conclusion, it can be said that the extinction of light in the galactic plane is such that (apart from exceptions) no object is visible in this plane at more than 8,000 L.Y. distance. Research on distant features of the Galaxy would be impossible by means of visible light alone. We shall see that the radiations of long wave length, which escape the absorption, now give us unexpected information.

QUANTITY AND DISTRIBUTION OF DIFFUSE MATTER
The total quantity of matter present in space in the neighbourhood of the Sun was evaluated by Oort by studying the order of magnitude of the components of stellar velocities normal to the galactic plane. There was found to be 6.10^{-24} gm./cm.^{3} and the stars represent two-thirds of this total. There remain 2.10^{-24} gm./cm.^{3} for the diffuse matter—that is to say, on the *average* about 1 atom of hydrogen per cc. Hydrogen represents the principal element of the Universe, and its atoms are at least twenty times as numerous as those of helium, which holds second place (and amounts to 20 per cent of the mass of the hydrogen). All the other elements together—atoms, molecules and dust—do not represent more than 1 per cent of the total mass. The gases show their

presence in interstellar space by selectively absorbing certain special radiations. It is in this way that in the spectrum of certain very distant stars the interstellar absorption lines make qualitative and quantitative analyses of the clouds of interstellar gas possible.

But these selective absorptions are, on the whole, not very effective. The losses of light in space arise essentially from general absorption, from the scattering of all the radiations by small solid obstacles. We have already stated that the most efficacious scattering particles have a diameter of some tenths of a micron. This dust, the chief agent of the opacity of the interstellar medium, is so effective that a minimal quantity is sufficient to explain the observed effects. We estimate the mass of the absorbing dust at one-hundredth the mass of the diffuse gases, namely only 2.10^{-26} gm./cm.^{3}.

Gas and dust show a chaotic distribution and in most directions every absorption line is multiple, owing to the different speeds of the separate clouds. The dust and gas show that they are intimately mixed; the gas carries the dust grains as impurities. The galactic plane is studded from place to place with these clouds like a dappled sky, and between the clouds the density of the matter is almost zero. In the middle of each cloud the density is about ten atoms of hydrogen per cubic centimetre (and more if we are considering dense, visible nebulosities). An average cloud has a diameter of 30 L.Y. and a mass equal to a hundred times that of the Sun; the distances between clouds seem to be about ten times as great, and their relative speeds from 5 to 10 km./sec. This rather low value explains why the diffuse materials are strictly confined to low latitudes. The clouds sometimes accumulate into vaster systems, a hundred times more massive (as in the regions of Taurus and Ophiucus). But an organisation of still higher order directs the distribution of the clouds or their systems, and it is they which delineate the spiral arms of our Galaxy. The spiral structure of our Galaxy has begun to be precisely described since 1950.

Gas and the arms. Baade, while studying the great spiral M 31 in Andromeda, established that the spiral arms are marked by supergiant stars and bright clouds, but in the interior of the nucleus the dusty arm, though continuing its course, is no longer bordered by supergiants. This shows that the arms have a primordial character and that the supergiants are born in them. The presence of very hot (young) stars in the arms gives rise to some interesting consequences. Almost all the interstellar hydrogen is in the neutral state and is cold (the kinetic temperature being of the order of $50°$ absolute — less than $—200°$ C). But when a very hot star is associated with a cloud, its ultraviolet radiation completely ionizes the surrounding hydrogen up to distances of 100 to 500 L.Y. The kinetic temperature in the interior of the ionized region (known as an H II region) exceeds in general $10,000°$. But these ionized clouds then become bright, because the recapture of the electrons by protons gives rise to well known light emissions (of which we observe, in general, only the Balmer series). These bright clouds associated with very hot stars of types O and B gave W. W. Morgan the idea of mapping the arms of our Galaxy by their alignments. Morgan, in 1951, thus established the existence of three concentric branches. The Sun lies at the interior edge of the middle arm, another branch passes closer to the centre of the Galaxy, and the third is distinctly further away towards the periphery.

These arms are inclined at 25° to the orbits described around the galactic centre, and the direction of the stellar rotation is such that the arms are 'winding up' —that is, they are 'following' the rotation of the nucleus. This sense of rotation is usual amongst the spirals.

RADIO-ASTRONOMY: THE SPIRAL ARMS AND THE
GALACTIC NUCLEUS

These results have been confirmed and extended since 1952 by Oort and his Dutch collaborators, thanks to an unexpected emission by cold hydrogen.

'*Forbidden*' *radiation of neutral hydrogen on the 21 cm. wave-length.* Cold hydrogen does not radiate, and it was at first very disheartening to be unable to examine this essential constituent of the universe because it was unaffected by external excitation. But in 1944 Van de Hulst showed that an emission un-observable in the laboratory could be predicted: the satellite electron of neutral hydrogen is capable of spontaneously turning on its axis of rotation, the rotations of the electron and the proton on parallel axes being capable of occurring in the same or the opposite senses. The transition takes place spontaneously on the average once in 11 million years, and the energy variation corresponds to a photon 21 cm. in wave-length. But space is so vast and the hydrogen atoms so numerous that the total energy is detectable. The cosmic wave of 21 cm. length was discovered simultaneously in the United States, Holland and Australia, in 1951.

As the different arms turn with different speeds, their emissions at 21 cm. are easily distinguished from one another, and a careful study of the line profiles at Leyden has been especially fruitfull. Not only does it confirm Morgan's results, but it considerably extends them. The outer arm has been followed for a distance of 60,000 L.Y., to a point nearly directly opposite the Sun with reference to the centre of the Galaxy. This is ten times as distant as visual views of that far side of the Galaxy could have been carried. The advantage of using the radio waves is that they are not absorbed like visible light: they pass unaltered across the most opaque 'coal sacks'.

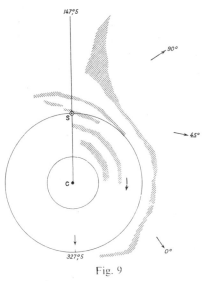

Fig. 9

Fig. 9 shows the outline of the arms of the Galaxy as mapped in the first survey made in Holland. The centre of the Galaxy is determined by means of radio waves with greater precision than by any other method, and the results very satisfactorily confirm the earlier estimates of the galactic coordinates—namely, $l = 327 \cdot 8°$; $b = -1 \cdot 5°$. Thus the traditional pole of the Galaxy (called *Ohlson's pole*) appears to be in error by about 1.5°. The distance of the Sun from the centre is 8·3 kiloparsecs and the velocity of the Sun in its rotation 216 km./sec.

Within the arms it is calculated that, on the average, there are two atoms of hydrogen per cubic centimetre, but this gas, as we have just seen, is concentrated in clouds of much higher density. Between the arms the density of the gas is practically zero. The width of an arm appears to be 2,500 L.Y., restricting it to the realm where the density falls to half the maximum density prevailing in the middle of the arm. Between the arms thus defined the distance from edge to edge would be about 5,000 to 6,000 L.Y. (twice the width of the arms). From longitude 55° upwards, the far distant arm appears to spread out in the shape of a fan. The same arm, towards $l = 50°$, appears situated north of the galactic plane, at a latitude 1·5° (and thus at 1,000 L.Y. above the plane of symmetry). The distant Cepheids in Cygnus are at a similar distance north of the galactic plane. We can see in this a residuum of the motions perpendicular to the galactic plane, which time would not have succeeded in eliminating in these distant regions. (At each oscillation of a cloud or star on either side of the galactic plane there is a brake on the movement through the action of the masses distributed in the plane).

The arms should play a rather important role by their gravitation in the direction perpendicular to the galactic plane, but in this plane their influence is limited because there the attraction of the central parts prevails. We can see the proof of this restricted action from the fact that the rotations, in our neighbourhood, are perpendicular to the direction of the centre, and that the differential rotation is regular in spite of the proximity of an arm inclined at 25° to our orbit.

The nucleus in the infra-red. J. Dufay and his collaborators at the Observatories of Lyon and Haute-Provence, extending Baade's researches, thought that by sensitizing the plates to infra-red it might be possible to obtain images of the star fields of the nucleus, using instruments of wide field (Schmidt telescopes). These attempts have fully succeeded: clouds still more dense and more extended have appeared on the fringe of the great star cloud of Sagittarius; the analysis of these shows that there we are actually dealing with the central agglomerations which have been revealed in outline by photoelectric techniques for some years.

The Milky Way and radio-astronomy. In 1932 Jansky noticed a radiophonic noise emitted by the Milky Way at wave-lengths of the order of a metre. In 1940 Reber compiled by radio-isophotes a chart of the intensity of the noise. This is concentrated in the galactic plane with a very pronounced maximum in Sagittarius and diminishes rather rapidly in the direction of the galactic poles.

At first it was thought to be radiation from interstellar material: then it was discovered that the ordinary stars, and in particular the Sun, had a radio emission which was not negligible, being considerably above that which their effective temperature theoretically allowed. Could the noise originally perceived represent the sum of the radiations from the hundreds of thousands of millions of stars of the Galaxy? The total energy appeared insufficient, but the discovery of powerful discrete radio-sources reopened the question of the origin of the 'background noise'. The supernovae and their residual

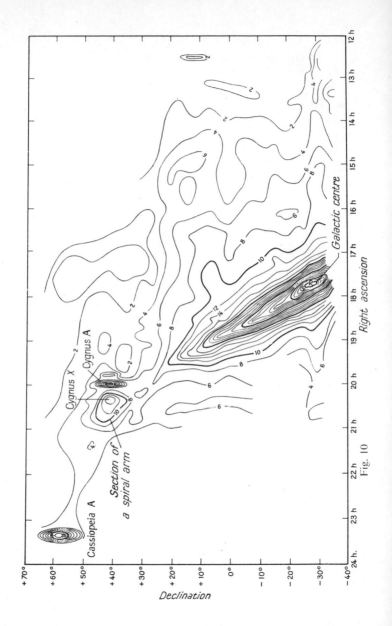

Fig. 10

nebulous filaments provide powerful radio emissions for periods of about a hundred thousand years. If these sources were more numerous than had been believed, and were suitably distributed, they might make the major contribution to the background noise. The question of the origin is, therefore, far from being settled.

However, radio-charts of the sky are none the less interesting for this. The one shown in Fig. 10 corresponds with the appearance which the firmament would have if our eyes were sensitive to radiations at $\lambda = 1 \cdot 20$ m. instead of being sensitive to those of about $\lambda = 0 \cdot 5\ \mu$. The curves of equal intensity are analogous to the contours of an Ordnance Survey map, and range from intensity 1 to intensity 70; they are seen to accumulate towards the centre of the Galaxy. The maximum of intensity 70 indicates the centre of the Galaxy with remarkable precision.

Equatorial co-ordinates	*Galactic co-ordinates*
$\alpha = $ 17h. 42m. 48s.	$l = 327 \cdot 8°$
$\delta = -28° 50'$	$b = -1 \cdot 4°$

Intense radio sources are scattered over the chart (they are elongated into an almond shape by reason of the differing directional sensitivities of the antenna in α and δ). Notice how the intensity in Sagittarius is much more striking in radio-waves than in visible light; this is because the radio-waves emanating from the nucleus reach us without absorption, whereas the light is enfeebled by the cosmic dust. In the same way, no visible star rivals in relative brightness the dazzling radio beacon known as Cassiopeia A (a nebulous filament).

The powerful source Cygnus A is even more extraordinary; it emanates from two spirals which are in

collision at a distance of 200 million light years
beyond the Milky Way. We can imagine the fantastic
power of this source for it to appear at such a distance with an intensity 37·5 (more than half the
maximum intensity of the nucleus of our Galaxy).

Notice, finally, towards the top of the figure the
almost circular concentric isophotes around Cygnus
X. Here is a 'plane section', so to speak, of the Orion-
Cygnus spiral arm, which, passing in the neighbourhood of the Sun, is lost in the depths of space in this
region.

THE DISTRIBUTION OF THE STARS IN THE GALAXY

In our vicinity certain types of very large and very
hot stars, recently born from the gas and dusts of the
arms, are strictly confined to the galactic plane: their
average distance from the galactic plane is of the
order of no more than 200 L.Y. Common stars like
our Sun are more distant from the plane, and their
average distance approaches 1,000 L.Y. Some peculiar stars, such as the RR Lyrae stars, have components of velocity perpendicular to the galactic plane
of the order of 65 km./sec. (like the globular clusters).
Therefore, we encounter these at average distances
of the order of 10,000 L.Y. from the galactic plane.

We see the kind of information regarding the
organisation of the Galaxy that the study of velocities
can give us. Oort has thus been able to construct a
model of the Galaxy by means of concentric ellipsoids, with increasing dimensions and decreasing
densities. The superposition and fitting together of
these adequately explain the observed facts. In this
way, the mean density of the galactic nucleus, where
two-thirds of the total mass are concentrated, has
been estimated to be *seven* times as great as the den-

sity in our vicinity. (Near the Sun, a cube of space with edges of 33 light-years encloses on the average a quantity of matter equal to eighty times the Sun's mass.)

Studies made in Holland on the distribution and radial velocities of neutral hydrogen, according to its emission of wave-length 21 cm., have furnished some very interesting results. In the first place, up to 10,000 L.Y. from the centre there appears to stretch a very turbulent layer of hydrogen, of thickness about 1,000 L.Y. In the direction of the centre the radial velocities observed for this turbulent gas attain 100 km./sec., and 50 km./sec. are found even at 5,000 L.Y. from the centre. This turbulence inhibits all localised structure and all trace of arms in this region; we are still ignorant of its cause. The density of the turbulent neutral hydrogen is low (1 atom per 2 cm.³)—one half of that in our regions—and we would be astonished at this if we had not reason for thinking that the hydrogen is largely ionised in the turbulent region. The protons do not take any part in the 21 cm. emission, but observation of a continuous emission in the vicinity of $\lambda = 21$ cm. shows that they are very abundant.

Between this disk of turbulent gas and the Sun, the two inner arms shown in Fig. 9 have been detected; their mean distances from the centre in this arc of their course are 16,000 and 21,000 L.Y. respectively. The nearer of these two arms to the Sun corresponds well with the associations of bright blue stars in the region of Scutum and Sagittarius, pointed out by Morgan, Whitford and Code. Previous measurements give the orbital velocities of rotation around the Galactic centre, at different distances from the centre. These velocities are shown in Fig. 8, the periods of revolution round the Galaxy being easily deduced from the lower curve. These numbers call for several comments.

The orbital velocities are of the order of 200 km./sec. and vary relatively little as we proceed from the gaseous nucleus defined above and come out to the neighbourhood of the Sun; that is to say, when the distance from the centre is tripled (from 8,500 to 27,000 L.Y., from P to S in the figure). But the *angular* velocity of displacement then decreases from 3 to 1; P makes three circuits in the Galaxy while S makes only one (in 230 million years). The lower curve in Fig. 8 shows the decrease of angular velocity; intermingling and dislocation of the vast clouds are favoured by this differential rotation. Contrary to former opinion, in the interior parts of our Galaxy there is no uniform rotation as with a solid, with constant angular velocity. (At least, this does not occur in the domain being considered here).

The orbital velocities, considered in a more refined way (upper curve in Fig. 8), present an interesting feature. They increase as we go out from the centre, pass through a maximum (226 km./sec.) around 21 to 22 thousand L.Y. distance, then decrease and attain 216 km./sec. at a distance of 27,000 L.Y. (the case of the Sun).

It is for this region passing from the maximum to the Sun and beyond, that the verification of the differential revolution has been made (Oort), and it then presents a Keplerian character; the velocity decreases when the distance increases (as in the revolution of the planets round the Sun). We see that if we can pursue the study of velocities in the direction of the galactic centre sufficiently far, the sign of the variation will change. We meet with the speed of the Sun again (216 km./sec.) at a point M, half way from the centre (the angular velocity of which is, in consequence, double that of the Sun). The point P, where the exact investigation ends, completes its orbit—its 'cosmic year'—in 80 million years, as against 230 million years for the Sun.

VARIATION OF DENSITIES AS A FUNCTION OF THE DISTANCE FROM THE CENTRE

The variation of velocities of rotation can lead to the determination of the distribution of matter in the interior of the Galaxy, assuming the variation of density to be continuous. In other words, ignoring the spiral structure, we seek only for the *mean* progressive decrease as a function of the distance. A hypothesis as to the flattening of the system (or rather, to the flattening of the concentric systems) is necessary, but such a hypothesis does not affect the significance of the conclusion if we make the necessary modifications to bring it within the limits of probability.

We know that the mean density of the Galaxy in the vicinity of the Sun is about 6.10^{-24} gm./cm.^{3}. This result was deduced over 20 years ago by Oort from the dynamic study of our neighbourhood. Censuses of stars and the evaluation of diffuse matter confirm this result.

The Sun belongs to a region where the matter is already very rarefied.

3

Stellar Populations
and the Evolution of Clusters

At the beginning of this century, Hertzsprung and Russell, studying all the stars for which the intrinsic luminosity (called the *absolute magnitude*) and the surface temperature (or the colour) were well known, made a remarkable discovery: the sets of characteristics possible to stars are strictly limited. Let us

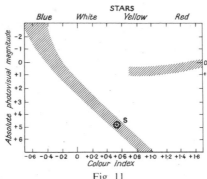

Fig. 11

represent on the abscissa axis the temperature, or the colour (colour index), or the spectral type (which is equivalent), and on the ordinate axis the absolute magnitude (or the intrinsic luminosity with reference to the Sun). Each star may then be represented by a point determined by these two co-ordinates. Instead of being evenly distributed, the points are found to be arranged on two rather narrow bands. (See Fig. 11.) One passes up the diagram in a diagonal from right to left. This is called the *main sequence*, the top portion of which on the left includes the brightest blue stars. The lower portion, on the right, is studded with *red dwarfs*, this part of the main sequence being called the *dwarf branch*. The Sun, which is a yellow dwarf, is shown in the diagram at S. Red dwarfs are very abundant in space. The other band, parallel to the abscissa axis, crosses the square at the height of $M = 0.5$. This is the *giant branch*; it does not join the main sequence, being separated from it by the 'Hertzsprung gap'.

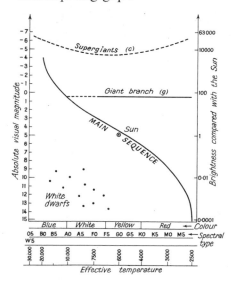

Fig. 12
Hertzsprung-Russell Diagram for the solar neighbourhood (Population I).

To simplify matters, we have not so far mentioned the *supergiants*. These stars are very rare in space but plentiful in our catalogues, for we can see them at immense distances. They are placed at the top of the diagram where they do not, however, form a continuous band (Fig. 12). In the lower left corner of

this diagram there are scattered some strange stars—
the *white dwarfs*—in which the matter is fantastically
dense and is known to be devoid of hydrogen. They
are stars in which the original hydrogen has been used
up.

This diagram, based on observation of our 'local
swimming pool', that is the immediate environs of
the Sun, has for a long time been accepted as repre-
senting the whole stellar population of the Universe,
and on it has been built—or attempts have been
made to build—a theory of stellar evolution. But in
fact, the diagram is concerned only with the population that we find in the arms of a galaxy or in their
immediate neighbourhood. We now call this the
diagram of Population I, and everything leads to the
belief that this population is not pure: it is a mixture
of populations of different ages.

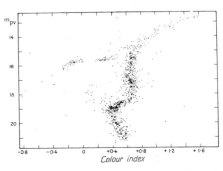

Fig. 13
Hertzsprung-Russell
Diagram for the globu-
lar cluster Messier 3
(Population II).
Ordinates: Apparent
photovisual magni-
tudes of the stars.

Observation of the globular clusters has revealed
a totally different diagram. Fig. 13 shows the distribution of the stars comprising Population II. This
population should be pure, because it has evolved in
isolation within the globular clusters. Baade has
shown that this population *predominates* in the
Universe; the nuclei of galaxies, the ellipsoidal

galaxies, and the disks of the spirals *between the arms*, are all formed essentially of Population II. This is a more general and older population; it no longer contains supergiants, in the absence of diffuse gas and dust.

The diagram of Population II is, in fact, characterised by the absence of supergiants and by the absence of the upper part of the main sequence. There remains in it the stump of the red dwarfs, which is identified with the corresponding part of the diagonal band of Population I when the two diagrams are superposed (Fig. 14). Population II includes a giant branch, but these are brighter than those of Population I. The apparent gap in this branch (Fig. 14) contains RR Lyrae stars (variables of short period) which have not been shown here. Finally, it is evident (Fig. 13) that a retrogression and a vertical branch join the stump of the dwarfs to the giant branch.

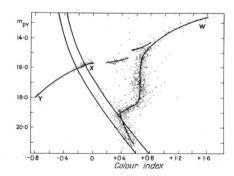

Fig. 14
Comparison of the preceding diagrams
The double curve represents the main sequence of Population I. Fig. 13 is compared with it by superimposing the red dwarf regions at the bottom.

In Fig. 14 the stump of the main sequence of M 3 has been superposed on the dark band which represents the main sequence of Population I. Recent studies (Baum) seem to show that serious displacements can take place, as in M 13 (a globular cluster in Hercules) especially, and also in M 3. The only factor that can account for these deviations is undoubtedly a different initial chemical composition; but it would be premature to insist on these results. It is only worth noting that the main sequences may not coincide; this will decidedly complicate the question of the populations.

INTERPRETATION OF THE DIAGRAMS IN TERMS OF THE EVOLUTION OF THE STARS

The stars evolve by the transmutation of their hydrogen into helium. The supergiants, which rapidly effect this transmutation, have necessarily a short life: they fade and disappear from our inventories. On the other hand, the economical dwarfs are able to survive for thousands of millions of years without changing much.

Explanation of the main sequence. Theoretical researches show that homogeneous models, that is, those in which the chemical composition of the matter is the same from the surface of the star down to its centre, resemble the real stars of the main sequence. The position at different points along the sequence depends on the *mass* of the star alone. The chemical composition by mass is, roughly speaking: hydrogen 80 per cent, helium 19 per cent, other elements 1 per cent. We are thus led to believe that the young stars, recently formed at the expense of the diffuse cosmic gas, are distributed along the main sequence.

The red giants. For a long time the great store of energy in the red giants was very puzzling, for their centres appeared to be too cold (according to the homogeneous models) to lead to the transmutation of H into He. The explanation lies in the consideration of non-homogeneous models in which a considerable part of the central hydrogen is assumed already transmuted into helium. This isothermal core of helium increases with time; to preserve its equilibrium the star must expand and thus become brighter, while maintaining its surface temperature. The

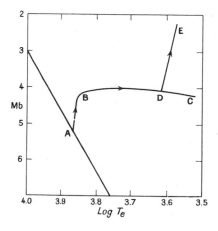

Fig. 15
Evolution of a star from the main sequence
Abscissae: Temperatures (given as logarithms).
Ordinates: Total (i.e. bolometric) absolute magnitudes.
A is a dwarf star on the main sequence (slanting line). It will evolve along ABDE.

evolution is shown by the curve AB (Fig. 15). Then, when this core of helium attains 12 per cent of the mass it contracts on itself, while the envelope and the surface of the star cool down; this transition is shown by BC. When the mass of the helium core attains 20 per cent of that of the star, a new turning point appears (at D Fig. 15) and the star then moves along the vertical branch of red giants (Figs. 13 and 15, DE). Later, when the mass of the helium core exceeds 50 per cent, its contraction can become such that its temperature is high enough for the transmutation of helium into carbon to take place. This reaction perhaps accompanies the movement of the star towards the left (WXY Fig. 14) while it completes the exhaustion of the hydrogen. Having reached Y, these stars would be blue dwarfs and the remainder of their life could lead them to become white dwarfs.

The theory makes it possible to know how much time will elapse until the stars born at different points in the main sequence arrive at the turn-off point of their evolution (Fig. 16). We see that for very bright stars this evolution is rapid; in the old clusters,

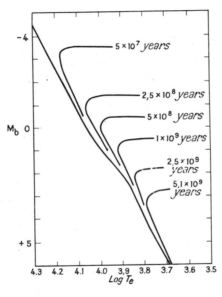

Fig. 16
Theoretical evolution of main-sequence stars
According to their initial characteristics, that is, according to their initial position on the main sequence, the stars evolve more or less rapidly, as shown in this theoretical diagram.

the upper stages will have disappeared. In short, when we examine different galactic clusters, we discover that their real diagrams bear a remarkable resemblance to preceding predictions and it is possible to attribute an age to them (Fig. 17). Thus, the Pleiades are young (some millions of years) but Praesepe and the Hyades, which have no more supergiants, are much older; their most advanced stars have already passed into the state of red giants on the right (the broken lines indicate the rapidity of the transition BC of Fig. 15). Finally, M 67 gives evidence of an age of 5,000 million years, and shows on the right a well formed vertical branch, as in the globular

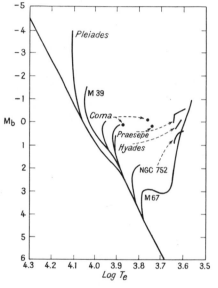

Fig. 17
Population of some open clusters (Population I).
Fig. 16 makes it possible to assign ages to them.

clusters of the same age (cf. Figs. 13 and 14). All these results, unknown until a comparatively few years ago, show the rapidity with which questions of stellar evolution are being clarified. Many difficulties remain, but the approaching years will not fail to resolve them.

AGES OF THE OPEN CLUSTERS OF THE GALAXY
Under the perturbative action of the other stars of the Galaxy, the feebly condensed clusters of stars tend to disintegrate, losing their stars by degrees. On the other hand, mutual collisions between the stars

within the cluster have a tendency to hold it together (with the occasional escape of one of the colliding stars). By submitting to analysis the results of these two contrary actions, we see that the disintegration would be *negligible*, even at the end of 10,000 million years, for compact masses such as the globular clusters, whereas the Pleiades lose half of their stars in 2,000 million years, and the Hyades will disappear in 3,000 million years. A cluster already loose, like Ursa Major, will be broken up in 500 million years. In brief, 3,000 million years are a *characteristic* interval for the evolution of an open cluster, and we recall that this is the order of time of the Earth's age. It is, therefore, difficult to relegate the open clusters to a much more ancient epoch in the past.

In spite of the present day appearance of super-giants in the arms of the Galaxy, we can believe that evolution will slow down and finally come to an end by the exhaustion of the diffuse gas. The globular clusters have led us to a past of 5,000 million years; this lapse of time seems also to fit in with the open clusters, the different rates of dispersal of which are being carefully checked. We are thus led to attribute to the entire Galaxy an age of the order of 5,000 million years *at least* (though it is felt that 10,000 million years would be excessive). Later on we shall see that the expansion of the Universe leads us to envisage a past of the same order of length.

The striking agreement of these cosmic clocks (the terrestrial crust, the Milky Way and its clusters, the globular clusters—satellites of the Galaxy—and the expansion), is perhaps the best reason that we have for believing in the *reality* of the expansion (page 121) and in a 'pseudo-origin' of the Universe; later on we shall justify this expression.

[*Palomar*]

Great Spiral in Andromeda, M 31. (48-inch Schmidt telescope.)
A, Giant and super giant stars of Population I in the spiral arms,
shown below enlarged and photographed in blue light. B, Stars
of Population II in the companion nebula NGC 205, shown
below enlarged and photographed in yellow light. Here, the
brightest stars are red; they are only one-hundredth as bright
as the blue giants in A.

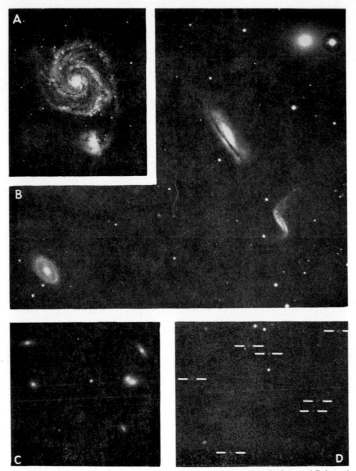

[*Mt. Wilson and Palomar*]

A, Spiral in Canes Venatici, NGC 4244 (M 51). (100-inch telescope.) B, Group of four galaxies in Leo; NGC 3185, type SBa; NGC 3187, type SBc; NGC 3190, type Sb; NGC 3193, type E2. (200-inch telescope.) C, Cluster of galaxies 40 million light-years distant, in Coma Berenices. (200-inch telescope.) D, Remote galaxies in Coma Berenices photographed at the limit of the 200-inch telescope. They are seen as faint patches in the gaps between the white lines drawn on the photograph.

4

Galaxies

About 1920 there was still a heated controversy in professional astronomical circles as to the existence or otherwise of objects in the Universe outside our own Galaxy. The controversy, moreover, was concerned chiefly with the following question: were the *spiral nebulae* intragalatic or extragalactic? Valid arguments (or what seemed such, in the state of knowledge of the period) were advanced on different sides, and in 1920 it could even be asked whether our Galaxy in itself constituted the whole Universe.

Since 1923-24 the situation was radically modified through the use of the Mount Wilson 100 inch telescope. Through it, the great neighbouring spirals, M 31 in Andromeda and M 33 in Triangulum, were resolved into stars and they show a structure similar to that of our Galaxy, with star clouds, open clusters, dark and bright shapeless nebulosities and satellite globular clusters. But, above all, amongst the giant stars which appeared there, Hubble identified Cepheid variables, which proved a first clue to their distances. These distances appeared at once to be so great—of the order of a million L.Y.—that they established not only the extragalactic character of the spirals, but their complete equivalence to our Galaxy at least in order of size. Thus the contents of the spirals have been identified in all their details with objects of analogous appearance which are found all along the Milky Way.

A more comprehensive inventory of space (we shall return to this later) showed that the spiral form is far from being predominant amongst the extra-galactic objects. The custom is now established of applying the name 'galaxies' to *all* the members of this family, by analogy with our Galaxy (which retains its initial capital letter to distinguish it).

On the other hand, the preliminary results suggested that our Galaxy was superior in size to all the others, and it was unsatisfactory to see the rebirth in this form of the idea that man inhabits a privileged part of the Universe. Two subsequent discoveries were necessary to restore our Galaxy to the rank of a bright but not an exceptional object. First of all there was the discovery of the feebly luminous outskirts of the galaxies, which meant that the diameters attributed to them would have to be doubled or trebled. Our Sun is situated in our Galaxy so near its edge that it would have belonged to one of the unrecognised regions for an observer situated in a neighbouring spiral.

The second discovery (dating from 1952) showed that we had under-estimated the distances of the galaxies. The distance of the nearest galaxies depends on the observation of their Cepheids, and in a series of masterly investigations carried out over some years Hubble, at Mount Wilson, succeeded in reassessing the data and extending the soundings to hundreds of millions of L.Y. But the basic unit of distance, the 'yardstick' so to speak, which is the distance of the Cepheids, was vitiated by a systematic error. Recent studies have shown that the Cepheids were four times as luminous as had been believed, and therefore twice as far off. It has thus been necessary to multiply all extragalactic distances by two.

Other factors, too, remain inexact and allow us to foresee a further increase in the estimates.

Be this as it may, this factor 2 of distance, (Baade's factor') has been responsible for doubling the diameters of the galaxies also. Added to the discovery of their outlying parts, this factor led to the discovery of many galaxies larger than our own. In particular, M 31 greatly exceeds us in the local group. Our Galaxy remains a very fine object, but not exceptional; anxiety has disappeared.

SUCCESSIVE CRITERIA OF THE DISTANCES OF THE GALAXIES

The modification of the unit of distance cannot alter the *ratios* of the distances suggested by Hubble for the distant galaxies. Let us here summarise the principles of his excellent work:

1. Utilising the Cepheids to determine the distances of the neighbouring galaxies.

2. Establishing that the brightest stars in each type of galaxy have always the same absolute luminosity.

3. Utilising these brightest stars (brighter than the Cepheids) as the standard of distance when we no longer see the Cepheids.

4. Recognising that the total luminosity of the larger galaxies in a cluster of galaxies is always the same, whatever the cluster (so long as it is a fair sample), and then finding the total luminosities of the nearby clusters from their distances as obtained by the preceding methods.

5. Applying this total luminosity to estimate the distances of clusters in which the individual galaxies are scarcely perceptible.

CLASSIFICATION OF THE GALAXIES

About 1900, Hubble proposed a classification of the galaxies in which the ellipsoids were first arranged in order of increasing flattening from the spheroid, EO, to the lenticular, E7. (See Fig. 2.) After the ellipsoids came the spirals, divided into two groups. First, there are ordinary spirals, S, where the arms start off from the nucleus itself, and then the barred spirals, SB, in which the arms start off from the extremities of a diametral bar. In both groups the indices a, b, c are used to indicate the relative importance of the nucleus and the arms. In the category Sa the nucleus predominates, the arms being rudimentary and formless. In Sb the nucleus is reduced in size, the arms being well developed and sub-divided. In Sc the nucleus is scarcely distinguishable and the arms are broken up into small patches or dots. The irregular galaxies ended the series.

Hubble never claimed to attribute an evolutionary significance to his sequence, although many commentators have seen in it the passage from a young to an old type of galaxy. It is also possible to regard the irregular type as young and the lenticular type E, afterwards spheroidal, as indicating the end of evolution, E's being the nuclei of type S galaxies after the arms had been dispersed. Nevertheless, the masses of E's do not seem to be *systematically* different from those of the S's. The present view is very different; the E type are galaxies denuded of gas; the S type are galaxies which have been able to develop arms because of the presence of gas.

In the great clusters, such as that shown in Fig. 18, where the only type found is E, Spitzer and Baade have shown that mutual encounters have cleared the galaxies of their gas, and this is why we do not find any spirals whatever the degree of flattening. The flattening depends solely on the angular momentum of each component object.

In the irregular galaxies or spirals endowed with gas, there has developed and still is developing a population of supergiants, blue stars of spectral type O, the absolute photographic magnitude of which can attain $M_{pg} = -7 \cdot 5$. The largest supergiants of Population I yield a hundred thousand times more energy than the Sun as measured photographically. The total population of the spirals is always mixed:

Fig. 18
Central region of the Corona Borealis cluster

Population I is always superposed on Population II (the primary, though the less spectacular). The ellipsoids, on the other hand, have a homogeneous population of Type II. Their largest stars are *red* (spectral type M) and their magnitude attains only $M_{pg} = -1 \cdot 5$ (one two-hundred and fiftieth of that of the brightest supergiants of the spirals).

The population of the ellipsoids is so uniform that their colour is remarkably constant. This colour is described by the number called the *colour index*. By photo-electric methods Stebbins and Whitford established that the ellipsoids near us have a mean colour index of 0·88 (this index shows that they are reddish), but the interesting fact is that the *dispersion* of indices, about this mean, is less than 0·10. This persistence has led to curious cosmological conclusions, as we shall see.

THE LOCAL GROUP OF GALAXIES

The galaxies have a strong tendency to group themselves; associations by twos, threes, fours or fives are frequent, but modern charts of the sky have shown that much richer agglomerations, in which the galaxies are grouped by dozens, by hundreds, sometimes by thousands, are numerous. So numerous are they that we ask today if these clusters do not touch each other—whether there exist between them regions for isolated and relatively *free* galaxies (galaxies of the 'general field', as they used to be called). We shall return to this subject, but for the moment let us assume that our Galaxy, with its two satellites—the Magellanic Clouds—belongs to a small *local group* of galaxies, of which we now know a score of members extending over 3 million L.Y. See the accompanying Table.

Its principal members have been known for a long time. Apart from the triplet just mentioned, there exist the great spiral M 31 in Andromeda, of type Sb like our own Galaxy, and its two ellipsoidal satellites, M 32 and NGC 205. According to the most recent calibrations by Baum (in 1954) at Mount Palomar, this triplet should be 2 million L.Y. from us. The

PRINCIPAL OBJECTS OF THE LOCAL GROUP

Object	Type	Apparent magnitude m_{pg}	Absolute magnitude M_{pg}	Apparent magnitudes of the brightest stars m_{pg}	Apparent diameters	Colour index	Number of associated globular clusters
1. The Galaxy	Sb						250
2. M 31	Sb	4·33	−19·6	16·0	197′ × 92′	0·86	None
3. M 33	Sc	6·19	−17·6	15·6	83′ × 53′	0·40	A few
4. Greater Cloud	Irr	1·2	−17·4	10·0	12°	0·25	—
5. Lesser Cloud	Irr	2·8	−15·8	?	8°	0·80	None
6. NGC 6 822	Irr	9·21	−13·9	15·8	20′ × 10′	?	—
7. IC 1613	Irr	10·00	−13·7	16·4	23′ × 23′	0·39	A few
8. NGC 205	E	8·87	−15·0	22·4	26′ × 16′	0·72	—
9. M 32	E	9·06	−14·8	22·4	12′ × 8′	0·90	2
10. NGC 147	E	10·46	−12·9	22·0	18′ × 18′	0·73	1
11. NGC 185	E	10·17	−13·2	22·0	14′ × 12′	0·74	None
12. Sculptor	E	8·8	−10·6	17·8	45′ × 40′	?	2
13. Fornax	E	9·1	−12·2	19·2	50′ × 35′	?	None
14. Leo II	E	13·2	−10·0			0·81	
15. Leo III	E	9·3	−13·0			0·87	
16. Draco	E	$m\text{-}M \simeq 19\cdot6$			$\simeq 1°$		
17. Ursa Minor	E	$m\text{-}M \simeq 19\cdot6$			$\simeq 1°$		
18. Wolf-Lundmark	Irr	11·13	−13·3	17·3	13′ × 16′		
19. Dwarf System		In course of study: co-ordinates α = 15h 14m, δ = 0° 05′ (equinox 1950)				?	

local group contains also a spiral, M 33, in Triangulum, of type Sc, situated in a direction near to that of M 31 and at a similar distance. Besides the Magellanic Clouds, still officially classified as irregular galaxies, the local group contains two other irregular galaxies, NGC 6,822 in Sagittarius and IC 1,613 in Cetus.

Regarding the ellipsoids, about a dozen have been counted. Apart from the satellites of M 31, we may point out the ellipsoids in the constellations of Sculptor, Fornax and Draco, the pair NGC 147 and 185 in Andromeda, and two dwarf systems in Leo, discovered in 1951 on the plates of the Mount Palomar sky map and similar to the Sculptor system. By their position these ellipsoids in Leo are of great importance, because up to their discovery our Galaxy was at the 'tip' in the local group, all the other members being seen from the same side, on one celestial hemisphere only. The ellipsoids of Leo are in the other hemisphere, extending the group in a new direction and withdrawing our Galaxy from its extreme position. Let us finally point out that in the course of the year 1953, three new dwarf galaxies were added to the local group; but we lack detailed information on them.

The local group is very difficult to define; admittedly it has a dynamic existence, and galaxies belonging to it are subject to its gravitation, but that gives us no information regarding its limits—either theoretically or practically. The objects which have an excessive radial velocity, for example, are reckoned as outsiders, but the word 'excessive' is naturally very ambiguous. Then, again, it is necessary to have a precise definition of a 'galaxy' and to obtain almost unanimous agreement on the definition. But, paradoxical as it may seem, this has never been done and disagreement exists even amongst specialists. Shall we give the name 'galaxy' to every cluster of stars not belonging to any recognised galaxy—even if it has merely escaped from one? Shall ten free stars—or a hundred or a thousand—wandering between galaxies consisting of thousands of millions of stars, bear the same name as these giants? Where is the limit?*

We should mention that the specialists of Mount Palomar keep in reserve a score of additional objects which may one day be added to the preceding Table. These are objects that are currently being studied, the distances of which are still uncertain. Most of them are small; a good many resemble open clusters or globular clusters of middling size (such as NGC 2,419). Need we call them *galaxies*, even if they are intergalactic?

To sum up, three spirals, five irregular galaxies (or presumably such) and eleven ellipsoids are the *recognised* members of the local group. Note the rarity of the spirals (15 per cent), and irregulars (26 per cent), compared with the large proportion of ellipsoids (60 per cent).

The examination of other groups confirms this predominance of the ellipsoids. We recall that in the richest and densest groups encounters between galaxies deprive them of their gas and 'arms' are never seen; the regular galaxies are *all* lenticular. Specialists conjecture that the stellar population of the ellipsoids is similar to—or even identical with— that of the globular clusters. Recent years have

---

*It is, perhaps, to this problem that we can trace the controversies regarding the light curve, that is, to the choice between Hubble's bell-shaped and Zwicky's hyperbolic curve. See *The Expansion of the Universe*, translated by J. B. Sidgwick, p. 79. (Faber & Faber, 1952).

greatly increased our knowledge of the population II of the galactic globular clusters (Cf. p. 58). We should like to be certain that the population of the ellipsoids is identical with that of the globular clusters, but for this purpose it would be necessary to identify stars of the *main sequence* in these galaxies, and to observe the characteristic turn-off point at B, in the colour magnitude diagrams of the ellipsoids (Fig. 15).

Unfortunately, the stars at B are dwarfs, hardly brighter than our Sun (and their absolute photographic magnitude is $M_{pg} = 3.5$.) Only the Draco ellipsoid is sufficiently close for us to hope to reach the point B with the 200-inch telescope on Mount Palomar and obtain the desired identification. In fact, the RR Lyrae variables of this system in Draco ($M_{pg} = 0$) are seen through the 48-inch Schmidt telescope, with apparent magnitude $m = 19.7$. Since the stars at point B are fainter by 3.5 magnitudes, we must look for them near $m = 23.2$. The 200-inch Hale telescope is the only instrument that could reach such high values of m. This study is in progress and emphasises the interest of the Draco Ellipsoid.

The ellipsoids are transparent: they are practically never associated with opaque areas. No doubt, the density of the gas is too low for the condensation of dust in it. Regarding the emission nebulae which have sometimes been described in them, these are undoubtedly cases of errors in identification; they may be merely 'planetary nebulae'—that is, stars with very extended atmosphere. Again, the presumed ellipsoids may be unrecognised spirals, with a sharp nucleus but with very indistinct arms. Walter Baade, the great specialist on this subject, asserts that he does not know any example of an indisputable ellipsoid endowed with genuinely characteristic nebulosities.

We shall now describe in some detail the satellites of the Galaxy—the Magellanic Clouds and the great spiral M 31.

THE MAGELLANIC CLOUDS

The Magellanic Clouds, in the vicinity of the south celestial pole, look like two detached fragments of the Milky Way, with a vaguely circular shape but with striking irregularities in their brightness. The Large Cloud extends in the constellation Doradûs over a region 7° or 8° in diameter, to a south galactic latitude of about 30°. Its apparent photographic magnitude is estimated as 1.2 (first magnitude). We are dealing here only with the main body, without bringing into the scene the extensions of faint luminosity (which would prolong the diameter to 20°). The Small Cloud, in the constellation Tucana, appears half as large and decidedly fainter: its magnitude is estimated to be 3 (to be exact $m_{pg} = 2.8$). It lies at a latitude of 45° south of the Milky Way.

The distances of these two Clouds from us are practically the same—of the order of 175,000 L.Y. This figure was derived from a study of the Cepheids, of the RR Lyrae variables and of the globular clusters belonging to the Clouds or in their immediate vicinity. A normal amount of absorption by matter in our Galaxy has been taken into consideration in fixing this result, but, in the absence of any knowledge on the subject, no account has been taken of any special absorption by any obscuring matter that might exist in the space between the Clouds and our Galaxy. We shall see that newly discovered 'bridges of matter' seem to unite the Clouds to our own system. The distance given, therefore, is liable to be modified if this new factor alters the brightness to an appreciable extent.

However that may be, the order of magnitude of their distance shows the Clouds to be *galaxies* of a greater size than the average, and naturally they are subjected to the powerful gravitation of our own Galaxy. They are, if we so wish to regard them, its satellites, but it would be inaccurate to consider them as simple fragments detached from the Milky Way. Their rather high latitudes would, in addition, be sufficient to condemn this hypothesis. They are two galaxies, existing as independent celestial objects, but associated with our Galaxy and with each other.

For a long time the Clouds have been classified amongst the irregular galaxies, but it is not impossible that they are barred spirals of a peculiar type. Their detailed study holds an obvious cosmological value. We are indebted to them for the discovery of the period-luminosity relation of the Cepheids, and if we had recognised their character as galaxies earlier, astronomy would—according to Shapley—have been saved several dozens of years of trial and error.

The Clouds are very different from one another. The Large Cloud contains many giant stars, blue and red, a large number of gaseous emission nebulae, among the brightest in the heavens (such as the Tarantula nebula), and many typical Cepheids; it is stocked with absorbing dust which completely conceals from our view the more distant galaxies that are behind it. It does not include a single short-period variable of the RR Lyrae type. It is considered that the Large Cloud has an *almost pure* population of Type I; nevertheless, some satellite globular clusters are known in it (Population II), but it could have encountered them in its course and annexed them.

The Small Cloud is very different. It does not contain dust; it is transparent and allows a view through itself of more distant galaxies without reducing their brightness or changing their colour to any appreciable extent. We therefore attribute to it a predominance of Population II. Nevertheless, it shows some gaseous emission nebulae typical of Population I. Its whole population, then, appears mixed, but radio-astronomical observations of neutral hydrogen on wave length 21 cm., made in Australia, have provided some new and rather surprising information.

The two Clouds have an extension in hydrogen appreciably greater than that of their visible stellar population. They nearly touch at their detectable gaseous boundaries, and we might almost ask whether they have not got a common hydrogen envelope. However, in the Large Cloud the distribution of the gas follows, in its main outlines, the distribution of its stars. More astonishing is the state of affairs in the Small Cloud, which, on account of its transparency, was believed to be poor in gas. Its hydrogen has been found to cover an area almost as large as that of the Large Cloud and includes even stronger concentrations of gas towards its centre. As to the envelope of gas, it extends well beyond the collection of its visible stars.

The Large Cloud appears to have a total mass of 2,000 million Suns, and the Australians estimate that its content in diffuse hydrogen is 30 per cent of this mass. A total mass of about one-third as much is credited to the Small Cloud, but this result is less accurate than the preceding one. Since this Cloud contains almost as much hydrogen as the first (4.10^8 Suns), we see that the mass of diffuse gas exceeds that of the matter agglomerated into stars; it is, perhaps, twice as much. The cosmological positions of the two Clouds are, then, very different.

Since the Large Cloud is rich in dust and the Small Cloud is almost destitute of it, the ratio of dust to gas is very different in the two Clouds. If, as we believe, the dust originated in the interior of the gas by the agglomeration of atoms (through the effect, in the course of time, of random mutual collisions), the absence of dust in the Small Cloud signifies either

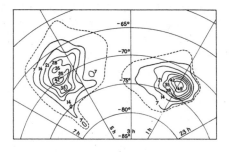

Fig. 19
Map of the Magellanic Clouds according to
their radio emission
Contours of equal radiation at $\lambda = 21$ cm.
The abundance of neutral hydrogen in each
region is proportional to the number given.
The Large Cloud is on the left.

that the conditions of formation have not been fulfilled (too low a density does not allow the formation of particles), or that the particles that were formed have been destroyed. Soundings on the 21 cm. wave show that the Large Cloud seen, if not face on, at least at an inclination close to the normal, is more irregular in shape than the Small Cloud; it is also flattened. These two characteristics conform to the properties of Population I. The rather irregular Small Cloud looks like a spheroid.

Soundings based on hydrogen bring substantial information about the gravitational ties which exist between the Clouds and also between them and the Galaxy. Fig. 19 shows a very clear elongation of the Small Cloud towards the Large, and an elongation

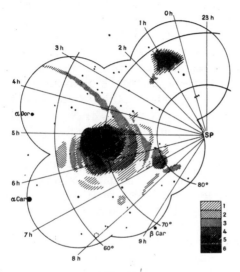

Fig. 20

Map of the outer regions and extensions of the Magellanic Clouds according to a mosaic of photographs pieced together. (*Right:* a scale of light intensity.)

of the Large Cloud towards our Galaxy, with a suggestion of an *antipodal* deformation in the Large Cloud. These results are in agreement with the photometric conclusions that de Vaucouleurs drew from a chart of the region, established by a mosaic of photographs (Cf. Fig. 20). It appears to be equally established that our Galaxy sends out, in the direction of the Large Cloud, an arm of matter drawn out by the tidal force. The existence of a corresponding antipodal galactic arm has not yet been shown as certain.

But the existence of all these phenomena is corroborated by the presence of very distinct connections between pairs of neighbouring galaxies—or between trios of galaxies—to which Zwicky has been drawing especial attention for some years. (See page 105). The measurements of the velocities made in the visible spectrum as well as by means of the 21 cm. waves show that each Cloud turns on an axis. Again, the two Clouds have a difference of radial velocity (with reference to us) of about 50 km./sec.; in other words, they form a *binary* system. The Sun's motion in the galactic rotation carries us away from them at more than 100 km./sec.

Population of the Clouds. The numerous Cepheids of the Small Cloud, to the study of which we owe the the first period-luminosity relation (a relation which has indeed served as a plumb line for the Universe) are redder than the classical Cepheids; they are of a special type (called W Virginis) and seem to characterise a population of Type II. The Cepheids of the Large Cloud, on the other hand, are normal (Type I).

The Large Cloud has *no* variable with a short period of the RR Lyrae type (Population II). The Small Cloud has few of them but it has some, thus confirming the existence of a Population II within it. The Large Cloud, opaque over almost all its extent, possesses some beautiful nebulosities and many supergiants (Type I). Its star S Doradûs is itself the most luminous star that is known (absolute magnitude $M_{pg} = -10 \cdot 5$), supernovae excepted. The brightest stars of the Small Cloud are much fainter.

MESSIER 31

No galaxy has been responsible for more progress in astronomy than this giant spiral in Andromeda. It was through the resolution of this 'nebula' into separate stars, through the identification of its Cepheids (Hubble 1923-24), and through the recognition of its globular clusters and its diverse supergiants, that the whole class of galaxies entered into astronomical science as the major units of the population of the Universe. In 1940, on plates sensitized to red (and specially to the red light of hydrogen), Baade succeeded in resolving the nucleus of M 31 into stars and discovered the fundamental stellar population, Population II; members of this Population II are even found between the spiral arms. Along the arms, Baade's negatives have revealed more than six hundred emission nebulae and the characteristic supergiants of Population I. The absorption of light in the regions between the arms is weak; many very distant galaxies are seen through them; in other words, one sees through Population II, which is devoid of a dusty medium. On the other hand, the arms of M 31 are opaque and are furnished with that absorbing dust which accompanies the gas. Baade showed that the gas and its dust represent the *fundamental* phenomenon; by their presence we can trace the outline of the arms and follow them to the centre of the nucleus. The supergiants were born in them; they are a secondary phenomenon, and the fact that the supergiants (with short lifetime) are seen in the arms proves that they are being formed there even in our own time.

In spite of the striking appearance of the arms of M 31, photometry establishes that the arms provide less than 20 per cent of the total light emitted by it.

Recent studies have, moreover, led to the discovery of very wide extensions to M 31, the wider areas consisting of a somewhat inconspicuous Population II. The two axes of the ellipse so familiar in photographs of this galaxy should really be multiplied by five. (The diameters given in Table A do not take into consideration the more faintly luminous extensions). The major axis of M 31 really extends over 5° in length, which makes it more than 200,000 L.Y. long (twice the diameter attributed to our own Galaxy).

ROTATION OF MESSIER 31

The study of the rotation of M 31 showed at first that the law of differential rotation, clearly observed in the Galaxy in the neighbourhood of the Sun, was valid only in outlying parts at a certain distance from

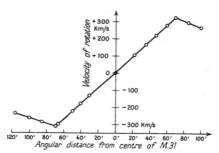

Fig. 21
Rotation of Messier 31

the centre. In fact, Mayall showed in 1950, from the radial velocities of 32 emission objects in M 31, that the velocity of circulation in this galaxy at first increases outwards from the nucleus; it then passes through a maximum and thereafter decreases. The same result was later obtained for our own Galaxy, first by means of the Cepheids, and then by radio-astronomy. This study further suggested that the distance of M 31 was at that time being grossly underestimated. In fact, judging by the velocities of the Cepheids in our own Galaxy, Mayall estimated that the maximum velocity occurred at about 25,000 L.Y. from the nucleus, whereas the maximum in M31 appeared at only half this distance.

In his conclusion, Mayall propounded the hypothesis that M 31, being similar to our Galaxy and of the same order of size, should be twice as far away as was believed. This forecast has been fully confirmed by Baade's researches (p. 96).

DISTRIBUTION OF THE GALAXIES

The counts of galaxies at first gave the appearance of an accumulation of them in the northern galactic hemisphere. Down to apparent photographic magnitude $17 \cdot 5$ there are found 45 galaxies per square degree in the northern hemisphere and only 26 in the southern. This dissymmetric distribution is purely fortuitous and is explained in great part by the existence of several rich clusters in the northern hemisphere, and relatively nearby, such as the Virgo cluster. But if we extend the magnitude to 19 the inequality disappears. The balance is afterwards maintained up to the limits of visibility ($m = 23$ at present). These results concern 500 million galaxies, and the homogeneity of the peopling of space, based on such vast numbers, already assumes a significant value. On the large scale we can say that the distribution of the galaxies still appears as approximately uniform, both in direction and in depth. In spite of certain affirmations to the contrary, no significant deviation has been found which could serve as the foundation of a cosmology based on heterogeneity.

In other words, nothing leads us to think that, in any direction, we are approaching a centre of agglomeration, or, conversely, a centre of dispersal of galaxies. The simplest and most correct picture would still be that of a Euclidean space regularly populated with galaxies, but there are large inequalities in detail which we shall now consider.

Up to what distance are the previous remarks valid? The giant telescope on Mount Palomar is certainly capable of seeing an average galaxy at a distance of $1\cdot5$ thousand million L.Y. and a giant galaxy at a greater distance still. But this instrument and instruments of the same kind have an absurdly small field of view (of the order of 1 per cent of the Moon's disk) and would require thousands of years to explore the whole of the celestial vault. Appropriate instruments for obtaining statistics are the wide-field Schmidt telescopes; a Schmidt of 48 inch clear aperture has functioned for eight years on Mount Palomar. Its field of good definition attains 40 square degrees—one hundred and sixty times the area of the full Moon—on each plate. In four years it surveyed, in two colours, the entire sky visible from the latitude at which it works. So far, we can say that its results confirm the homogeneity of the peopling of space by galaxies out to a distance of the order of 800 million L.Y.

This macroscopic result leads us to hope with some confidence that the Universe is nothing more—and nothing less—than a single, vast system of galaxies, homogeneously distributed on the large scale. Of course we should not consider this view as beyond dispute: we have too often seen cosmologies abruptly superseded through a decisive advance of knowledge, with fundamental changes. Nevertheless, human cosmologies acquire more plausibility in proportion as they are based on the investigation of a wider domain. The stage that has extended our perspective from a field of stars to a field of galaxies represents, without any doubt, a decisive and definitive advance. The very conditions under which the field of galaxies has progressively revealed its characteristics logically allows but little expectation of a further sudden change. Furthermore, considerations of the practical limitations to sudden extension of our investigations much farther into space does not afford much hope of a major advance analogous to that which led from the Galaxy to our present limits. In what follows, we shall, therefore, take the sample of the Universe which we have under observation as representative.

The Clusters of Galaxies. For a long time the tendency of galaxies to occur in small groups had been remarked upon, and later some two or three dozen much larger clusters were observed. Some of these contained hundreds, or even thousands, of galaxies in crowded formation. We have already noted that the existence of the great northern clusters at first gave primacy to the north galactic hemisphere, but this impression was found to be due to the fact that the statistics were not being applied to a sufficiently large domain.

The existence of the clusters seems to falsify our conclusions relative to the *homogeneity* of the peopling of space, but actually it does nothing of the kind. The homogeneity applies to realms that are sufficiently large for the effect of one cluster to be negligible. In other words, what we have found is homogeneity in the distribution of the *clusters*. The 48 inch Schmidt telescope at Mount Palomar, which has completed a chart of the sky visible at its latitude, has revealed more than six hundred large clusters of galaxies.

Another chart of the sky has been finished at the Lick Observatory, in California, with a smaller astrograph, but the analysis of the data is more advanced. The opinion of the Lick experts is that the galaxies exist *only* in clusters. In particular, each cluster seems to be much larger than had been imagined. Gravitation has a kind of sifting effect, causing the most massive and brightest galaxies to gather towards the centre. The light objects, endowed with greater speed, are able to travel in longer orbits so that they are encountered in great numbers at considerable distances from the centre. Attention was originally focused only on the beautiful accumulation of large compact galaxies in the nuclei of the clusters; but statistics embracing wider fields have revealed the vast extensions of the clusters and a super-abundance of small objects.

Statistics compiled (chiefly by Zwicky) with the 48 inch *Schmidt* telescope on Mount Palomar, carried up to magnitude 19, show that the formerly published diameters of the clusters must often be multiplied by three, sometimes by eight or ten, and the population increases in a surprising manner. Thus, the cluster Coma I, formerly called *Nebelnest* (the nest of nebulae) by Wolf, and of which the two greatest galaxies are of magnitudes 13·2 and 13·5, was supposed to extend over 1·7° and to include 800 galaxies. Zwicky showed that its diameter is at least 12° and that, in this area and down to the 19th magnitude, the cluster contains nine thousand galaxies (in addition to the number supplied by the surrounding general background). The distance of the cluster is 120 million L.Y.; its real diameter should thus exceed 20 million L.Y. At the same time, the multitude of clusters has appeared to be such that, taking into consideration the new dimensions of each cluster, they now seem to be contiguous.

We can readily believe that a fast-moving galaxy may escape from its original cluster and become relatively free. But we should ask ourselves whether there exists much free space between the clusters, and whether a 'free' galaxy does not soon fall into the sphere of attraction of a neighbouring cluster. However that may be, the view is now established that the majority of the galaxies belong to clusters the centres of which seem to be distributed in an almost uniform manner. But we should modify this concept with a further new discovery: the clusters themselves have a strong tendency to be grouped into *clusters of clusters* (the nearer clusters forming families of two, three, or more).

By way of example, Fig. 22 represents, according to the Lick chart, two regions of the sky in which the contours of equal density of galaxies are shown by curves analogous to the contours on a geographical chart. In these two regions the faintest galaxies (magnitude 18·3) are shown with a *mean* density of eighty galaxies per square degree (from sixty to a hundred according to the locality under consideration). The clusters are shown on the chart of the sky as mountains are shown on a geographical chart: the contours congregate around a culminating point. In the first area (15 square degrees), there are five hundred galaxies over and above the average number, distributed in two main condensations: the density attains 200 at the upper maximum point and 180 at the other.

The lower area, *b*, concerns 25 square degrees,

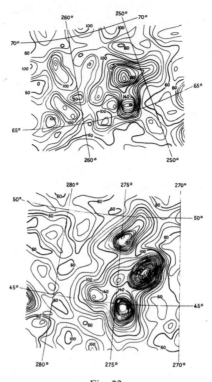

Fig. 22
Two clusters of clusters of galaxies

where there are 1,400 galaxies over and above the
average number, grouped in three adjacent clusters.
Their respective maxima are 200, 280 and 250 objects
per square degree above the mean level of 80. Two
small condensations (up to 160) will also be noticed
in the vicinity of the three large ones—on their edges,
we might say. These five associated clusters may be
placed at a distance from us of 200 million L.Y. The
diameter of clusters worthy of attention always

exceeds a million L.Y. and attains 5 or 6 millions in the average clusters; it exceeds 10 millions in the large clusters, but we have suggested 20 millions for the giant cluster Coma I (p. 86).

From the first, the clusters of galaxies have played a great role in cosmology. A rich cluster affords a complete sampling of galaxies, informing us of the frequency and the relative luminosity of the different types. The nearby clusters have shown that the galaxies of highest luminosity in all rich clusters have a 'standard' luminosity which enables the Universe to be sounded. In other words, in spite of the variety of luminosities of the galaxies (which range from 1 to 1,000 or 10,000, and perhaps more), there is a 'ceiling' of brightness. The value of this in assessing the distance of a cluster is, perhaps, not very high, for it is possible that far fewer clusters contain such complete collections of typical galaxies as had at first been believed. The rich and crowded clusters show only lenticular galaxies, devoid of spiral arms. Their mutual collisions (or partial collisions) have removed the gas from these galaxies, which henceforth evolve poorly (in the morphological sense). This is the theory of Baade and Spitzer. For example, in the Corona Borealis cluster, about 350 million L.Y. away (see Fig. 18), we see nothing but spindles with highly condensed central nuclei. All the usual degrees of flattening are observed, but we never see spiral arms or dark equatorial bands. In proportion as the flattening increases and the spindle lengthens, the central nucleus diminishes. Here we are dealing with a series similar to the classical series, but the absence of gas has radically modified the appearances.

The Virgo Cluster. We cannot pass by in silence a very beautiful cluster with more than 3,000 galaxies in the constellations of Virgo and Coma Berencies. Its brightest objects are of the tenth magnitude and the central part of the cluster occupies about twenty degrees, but the peripheral population runs into Ursa Major and Lynx to the north, and can be followed to Centaurus in the south. Thus, this fine cluster possibly exceeds 60° in diameter, and its centre is about 30 million L.Y. distant. If its radius reaches 10 million L.Y., as it may do, it is not impossible that the small local group of galaxies, to which we belong, should be an appendage of this vast agglomeration.

However this may be, the Virgo cluster has played a primary role in modern cosmology. It was the first one to show the existence of great agglomerations of galaxies: it served as a standard collection to the pioneers Hubble and Shapley. Furthermore, it has provided galaxies in which the stars (at least, the supergiants) were able to be resolved at Mount Wilson, and this has made possible a comparison of the total luminosity of the galaxies with that of their brightest stars. The Virgo cluster has thus served as a laboratory for establishing gauges for soundings into remoter regions where the stars are no longer seen, and where only the total luminosity of the galaxies can be observed. Finally, the Virgo cluster marked the frontier of human investigations in 1928, when Hubble published the law of the expansion of the Universe, of which we shall soon speak. At present the soundings extend to distances nearly fifty times as great.

5

The Spectral Shift of the Galaxies

We have already described (p. 10) the phenomenon known as the Doppler-Fizeau effect. We saw that the radial motion of a star with reference to an observer involves a displacement of the spectrum proportional to the relative speed of the object. If this motion is a recession, the shift takes place towards the red end of the spectrum.

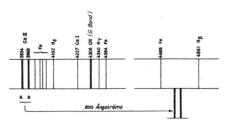

Fig. 23

Record red shift in the spectrum of a galaxy

The so-called H and K absorption lines of ionised calcium Ca II, in the extreme ultra-violet, are shifted through 800 Angstöms and appear in the neighbourhood of the blue Balmer line Hβ of hydrogen in the comparison spectrum.

The spectra of the galaxies show a shift towards the red, as if they were running away from the observer—that is, from our own Galaxy (Fig. 23). The shift shows all the characteristics of the Doppler effect, and in particular, $\Delta\lambda/\lambda$ is found to be independent of the wave length selected in the spectrum (the verification being accurate to about 1 per cent). But it presents in addition a most astonishing property: it is proportional to the distance of the galaxy considered, as though the galaxies were running away from us with a speed proportional to their distance!

It is always permissible to describe the red shift by expressing the speed which would correspond to it if the ordinary Doppler-Fizeau effect be assumed, and at the same time to reserve the opinion that the matter is really a more complex phenomenon. The speed thus given is therefore symbolic, and even if the red shift is not actually a Doppler effect, we still indicate it as a 'speed of recession'. The acceptance of a real recession explains the spectral shifts, but would imply an expansion of the system of galaxies for which it is advisable to discover the cause. If, however, we reject the recession, the incontestable (and fantastic) reddening of light of the galaxies, confirmed about 35 years ago, still remains unexplained. None of the explanations so far proposed has been accepted as valid.

This is why, pending a proof to the contrary, the author of this book and the greater number of contemporary astronomers consider the recession as real, the more so because independent theoretical reasons also lead to the view that the Universe is unstable and expanding. The discovery of the fundamental phenomenon deserves to be described.

The pioneer was Slipher, at Flagstaff (Arizona). Between 1912 and 1922 Slipher established the radial velocities of forty-two galaxies and recognized that they were largely positive, the record being $+1800$ km./sec. A small number of exceptions concerning the neighbouring galaxies was explained by the rotation of our own Galaxy. Thus, M 31, in Andromeda, is approaching us with a speed of 300 km./sec. principally because the galactic rotation carries us in its direction at a rate of about 200 km./sec. The residue of 100 km./sec. could be explained by a relative motion of M 31 and our Galaxy in the local group.

When Hubble discovered the Cepheids in the neighbouring galaxies (in 1923-24) he undertook to measure the distances of all the nebulae of which Slipher had obtained the radial velocities, by calibrating the supergiants of these galaxies. In 1928 he published the law of spectral displacements—called Hubble's Law—which is currently interpreted as a *distance-speed* relation. The red shift is found to be proportional to the distance; in other words, the velocity of recession is proportional to the distance. This law was established as far as the Virgo cluster, which implies that its scope was supposed to be from 7 to 8 million L.Y. The velocity of recession seemed to increase by 160 km./sec. per million L.Y. distance. The velocity of the Virgo cluster is about 1,240 km./sec. (the value established today by means of thirty-two radial velocities of galaxies which form part of it).

We know today that the distances found by Hubble were on the average only one-third of the correct values, whereas the speeds were correct. The *constant of recession* appears today to be near 55 km./sec. per million L.Y. (instead of 160). Using the 100-inch telescope on Mount Wilson, from 1928 to 1936, Humason studied the radial velocities of the brightest ellipsoidal galaxies (the easiest to study) of more and more distant clusters, while Hubble was attempting to find their exact distances from their luminosities. The record of velocity was progressively pushed forward up to 40,000 km./sec. for a cluster in Boötes, and the law remained linear.

To go further out, the more powerful 200-inch Hale telescope on Mount Palomar was necessary. Humason took the record to 61,000 km./sec. with a certain cluster in Hydra, the distance of which should be close to 1,100 million L.Y. (Fig. 23). The law remains *linear* within the limits of errors of the measurement of the distances, but we shall see that this measurement is, unfortunately, still very imperfect. We may here remark that according to eleven measured velocities, the galaxies of the local group show no systematic displacement of their spectrum; in other words, the expansion—if there is an expansion—plays no part for the local group. The *interior* gravitation of the clusters seems stronger than the *cause* of dispersion, which, as we have seen, acts between the clusters.

At the present time the radial velocities of eight hundred galaxies are known, and they are regularly arranged between 0 and 61,000 km./sec. (more than one-fifth of the velocity of light). The phenomenon is continuous and applies to all types of galaxies in all directions of the sky (accessible from California). In particular, the law is valid for the two celestial hemispheres. The velocities indicated by Humason are certainly exact to about 1 per cent or 2 per cent when they refer to remote clusters (the velocities of rotation in the clusters becoming negligible in comparison with those of the recession). This precision is confirmed when several galaxies are measured in the same cluster. Thus, the Corona Borealis cluster, already mentioned, shows *eight* radial velocities of galaxies that are in agreement. The uncertainty of the velocity-distance relation rests exclusively on the determination of the distance.

Before further discussion we shall consult Hubble's figure (Fig. 24), published in 1953, some months before his death. There we see in the ordinate the velocity—or rather the logarithm of the velocity—and in the abscissa the apparent magnitude of the tenth brightest galaxy of each cluster. This magnitude

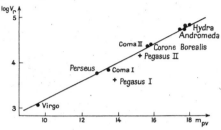

Fig. 24

Relation between apparent magnitudes and velocities of galaxies (Hubble, 1953).
Ordinates: Logarithm of speed of recession.
Abscissae: Magnitude of the 10th brightest galaxy in each cluster.

The observed points lie on a straight line ($\log V = 0\cdot2m + 1\cdot16$).

(photovisual) represents the distance of the cluster, and Hubble chose the tenth brightest galaxies (in place of the brightest) to avoid the contingency of exceptional objects: the tenth is a more stable criterion than the first.

THE DIFFICULTIES IN THE MEASUREMENT
OF MAGNITUDES

The measurement of the distances of the galaxies involves a great number of difficulties, not all of which have been overcome. Without entering into details, it is advantageous to understand the nature of these difficulties.

The unit of extragalactic distance. We know how the Cepheids gave us information on the distances of the nearest galaxies and how Hubble, basing his work on their absolute magnitudes—supposed known—established the criteria which have led us to the frontiers of the realm explored.

But the Cepheids are rare supergiants: none of them is sufficiently near to show a sensible trigonometrical parallax. In default of anything better, Hertzsprung established the luminous power of the Cepheids by basing it on eleven very small proper motions provided by the Preliminary General Catalogue (PGC). It is on this precarious result (precarious because its value is purely statistical and the proper motions were doubtful) that we had to rely for a long time.

In 1952 Baade, by a study of M 31 through the Hale (200-inch) telescope, showed that the accepted distance for M 31 was about half the true distance. Hence the Cepheids in it are twice as far away and have four times the luminosity that was previously accepted. Our *standard of distance*, which is based on these, was therefore only half the true value, so all the extragalactic distances had to be multiplied by two. For a young science like astrophysics such rectifications need not cause any surprise. We may, then, consider that this systematic error has now been really corrected. Recent trustworthy fundamental catalogues furnishing certain proper motions of Cepheids confirm Baade's work; further, a dozen other researches of a different nature have confirmed Baade's factor of 2.

Unfortunately, other causes of error are of a more serious nature. It has been pointed out (Cf. p. 9) that the distance of a galaxy is based on a knowledge of its distance modulus (m—M); it is, therefore, necessary to measure m, the apparent magnitude of the galaxy, and to know correctly its absolute magnitude M.

The measurement of apparent magnitudes (m). *Comparison stars.* The measurement of (m) really involves many hazards. First it is necessary to have some comparison stars the standard magnitudes of which should be certain up to the limits of visibility ($m = 23 \cdot 3$ at present). But hitherto there have been no catalogues of faint stars because we had no need of them. The Mount Wilson astronomers, with the aid of photoelectric cells, have had to compile some photometric catalogues indicating series of reference stars, at first down to $m = 18 \cdot 5$, and then down to $m = 21$. Today, we work between $m = 21$ and $m = 23$. The poor quality of the magnitudes of the reference stars utilised by Hubble between 1930 and 1940, before these recent studies, has had an unfortunate consequence: the system of magnitudes which he proposed for the galaxies is not only inaccurate in absolute values, but it is not homogeneous, which is more serious. A single correction (such as that of Baade) could not restore his results to their correct values.

Determination of the magnitude m *of galaxies.* The galaxies have pale, indistinct images, lacking in contrast. The total luminosity increases sensibly when we take into consideration the feebly illuminated areas which may extensively surround the conspicuous primary body. It is only a few years ago that we learned to measure correctly the 'integrated' luminosity of galaxies. At Mount Wilson and Mount Palomar great efforts are being made with all the resources of modern physics. Photo-electric cells are being used to scan the images area by area, by moving the photographic frame, and filters of different colours are being employed.

Determination of the absolute magnitude M *of standard galaxies.* Baade's coefficient of 2 has already corrected the value of M by $-1 \cdot 5$ (a number which corresponds to quadrupling the luminosity in the conventional scale). But the discovery of faintly luminous outskirts immediately introduced new difficulties, for since the galaxies chosen as prototypes are nearby their outskirts are found to extend well outside the field of the telescopes used. A photometer will easily collect all the light of a galaxy that is distant enough to give a small image, but it will not be able to do so for an object like M 31 (p. 81). We should, then, divide up the image, evaluate separately the luminosities of the small areas thus defined, and integrate the results. The luminosity of the galaxies has been, up to a recent period, very much underestimated.

Effect of the red shift on the magnitudes (m) *of galaxies.* The energy W of a photon is decreased if its wave-length increases. All the photons that contribute to the formation of the image of a galaxy are enfeebled by the spectral displacement: the percentage of weakening is equal to the relative displacement $\Delta\lambda/\lambda$ (which attains 20 per cent for the nebulae in Hydra, the most distant ones known at present). But it is necessary to correct the measured magnitude (m) and to find the magnitude that the galaxy would have if the displacement did not exist, in order to establish the distance modulus. Without such correction the enfeeblement of the image would be taken for the effect of the distance, whereas it is here due to the red shift of the spectrum. The correction is difficult because the photographic plate receives only a small portion of the total light; when coloured filters are used, only a narrow band of rays, B (Fig. 25), is concerned in the formation of the image. But if the spectrum is displaced, the energy collected is that proceeding from B'. To correct the magnitude, it is then necessary to know the *curve E of the energy distribution* in the spectrum of the galaxy studied.

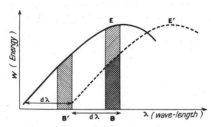

Fig. 25
Apparent magnitudes of distant ellipsoidal galaxies
Abscissae: Wave-length.
Ordinates: Corresponding energy.
E, energy distribution in a nearby ellipsoid; E', energy distribution with a shift dλ for a distant ellipsoid; B, pass band; B', energy actually received.

To facilitate matters only the distant ellipsoids were studied, and in 1947 Stebbins and Whitford established the energy curve of a nearby ellipsoid, M 32, a satellite of M 31. All subsequent corrections are based on this single investigation and it is urgently required that other neighbouring ellipsoids should be submitted to the same analysis. The fact that the spectrum and the colour of neighbouring ellipsoids are remarkably constant gives confidence in the preliminary result.

The Doppler-Fizeau correction. Matters are more complicated if the spectral displacement is due to a recession, for not only are the photons received enfeebled, but the *number* of photons received in a unit of time is reduced in the same ratio. Taken by and large, a correction $\Delta m = \Delta \lambda / \lambda$ is to be deducted from the measured value of m if the phenomenon is a recession (up to $\Delta m = 0 \cdot 2$ for the Hydra cluster).

This correction was deliberately omitted by Hubble in Fig. 24. If we introduce it, the Hydra point will slide $0 \cdot 2m$ towards the left; the representative line will become a curve slightly concave towards the top and that would indicate a small *acceleration* of the phenomenon of recession with the distance (instead of a *linear* law of recession).

But the uncertainties prevailing in the measurement of m do not yet allow us to choose between the linear law and the occurrence of acceleration; Hubble frankly admitted this in 1953.

THE SCALE OF DISTANCES

For all these reasons, the distances proposed in 1936 by Hubble were not mutually consistent. Baade's coefficient of 2 allowed a single systematic correction to be made, but the correction of the magnitudes for extraneous effects (even apart from the intervention of intergalactic matter) is still very difficult.

The determination of the photo electric magnitudes of eight hundred galaxies of which the radial velocities are known, has been accomplished in California. It is estimated that the precise examination will require four years, but Sandage now cites some results of the whole work which appear relevant.

1. Hubble's law remains *linear* up to a distance which is, on the whole, sixty times as great as that to which it was applied in 1928.

2. The value of the corrected recession is about

55 km./sec. per million L.Y. (instead of the 160 proposed in 1936 by Hubble).

3. The relation is valid for *all* directions of space and is consistently verified for all distances. In other words, the relation is isotropic, homogeneous, and established in a continuous manner.

4. The *mean* multiplication factor for the distances needs, apparently, to be 3 (Baade's coefficient included).

But this last factor varies according to the object, since the initial results were heterogeneous. The Virgo cluster is situated 30 million L.Y. away (instead of 7) and the group surrounding the fine nebula M 81 in Ursa Major requires a coefficient of 4 (a distance of 7 million L.Y. instead of the 1.7 proposed by Hubble).

W. A. Baum's Recent Investigations. The spectroscopic method has enabled astronomers to obtain reliable measures of the velocities of galaxies up to 60,000 km./sec., or one-fifth the speed of light. The largest value corresponds to a cluster of galaxies, the brightest members of which have magnitudes between 17 and 19. Even on Palomar, it has not been possible to carry the examination of spectra any further owing to the brightness of the night sky, which fogs the plate after a long exposure and thus obscures details in the spectra of very faint galaxies. However, it is possible to obtain images (albeit not dispersed into spectra!) of galaxies that are one hundred times fainter still (down to $m = 23$).

W. A. Baum has developed a very promising photoelectric method of measuring the spectral red shift without dispersing the light. Curve E (Fig. 25) is effectively determined from a small number of points (six, in practice). The method consists in simply measuring the energy received from a galaxy in six different spectral regions defined by 6 colour filters (an ultra-violet region and blue, green, yellow, red and infra-red regions). True, the use of a glass filter to admit a well-defined 'colour' reduces the energy received, but much less so than does dispersion; furthermore, photo electric cells have now reached such a high degree of amplification (of the order of 10^9) that the filtered radiation is still measurable about 4 magnitudes below the spectrographic limit. Thus an immense new field has been opened up for the study of galaxies, and it is in this new field that tests of the expansion of the Universe will be found.

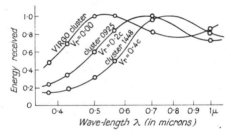

Fig. 26

Red shifts measured photo-electrically from the energy distribution curve as a function of wave-length.

The speed of recession of the Virgo cluster is practically zero in relation to those of the clusters compared with it; the curve for the Virgo cluster can thus be used as a reference.

In an initial application of his method, Baum studied the energy distribution curve obtained from two ellipsoidal galaxies of the 19th magnitude in a very remote cluster (No. 1448) and compared it with those obtained from the Virgo cluster galaxies and from one of the two clusters holding the previous record in velocity (No. 0925).

The results are shown in Fig. 26. The displacements of these two curves to the right compared with that of the Virgo cluster are striking and the last red shift is double the previous one (the horizontal scale, of wave-length λ, is logarithmic). In other words, cluster No. 1448 recedes at a velocity of 120,000 km./sec., that is to say at two-fifths of the speed of light.

This result prolongs the straight line of Fig. 24 in a remarkable way. The *magnitude-velocity* relation remains strictly linear over a range of velocities that has been doubled, that is to say in all probability throughout a volume of space that has been multiplied by 8. No curvature of the graphical relation is perceptible, either upwards or downwards.

Recent extension of measurements of the red shift through radio-astronomy. We have mentioned (p. 91) that the relative red shift $\Delta\lambda/\lambda$ is constant throughout the length of a *spectrum* (i.e., approximately between $\lambda = 0.3$ and 0.6 micron). Radio-astronomy has recently provided a proof that $\Delta\lambda/\lambda$ remains constant through an immensely wider range, namely up to $\lambda = 21$ cm.

In fact, the very powerful radio source Cygnus A (p. 51 and Fig. 10) is the result of a collision between two galaxies for which the red shift in the *visible* spectrum indicated a recession of 16,800 km./sec. Observation of the absorption line of neutral hydrogen in the short-wave radio region ($\lambda = 21.1$ cm.) shows it to be shifted by over 1 centimetre ($\lambda = 22.3$ cm.). The radio-astronomical radial velocity deduced from this is 16,700 km./sec., within an accuracy of 50 km./sec. This result is thus practically identical with that inferred from the visible spectrum and assures us of the perfect constancy of the ratio $\Delta\lambda/\lambda$ (with an accuracy of one thousand millionth over a range of 1000 angströms). Moreover, we learn that the red shift does not alter the *hyperfine* structure of spectral lines, since the 21 cm. line is a hyperfine transition.

These new facts give great strength to the interpretation of spectral red shifts in terms of real velocities of recession; that is to say, they reinforce the theory of the expansion of the Universe.

INTERGALACTIC MATTER

Up to the present, the evaluation of the mean density of the Universe, the measurement of the magnitudes of galaxies and of their colours, have taken no account of the presence of 'intergalactic matter. However, Zwicky has given many proofs that such matter does exist. At the moment we are in a similar position to the astronomers who studied the Galaxy towards 1930, and who discovered with some trepidation that the galactic dust and interstellar gases had falsified most of their previous measurements. What we now hope is that the indisputable material which peoples the space between galaxies may not have too great an influence on our present evaluations. Naturally, until clear proofs of such influence are forthcoming everyone will be disposed to be satisfied.

Proofs of the existence of tenuous material in the supposed intergalactic void are as follows:

1. Calculation (and simple common sense) show that materials endowed with sufficient velocity can leave the galaxies and fly off into the intergalactic void. Zwicky has taken pains to point out stars or clusters of stars which might have escaped from our Galaxy. He found blue stars of faint apparent magnitude in the direction of the poles of the Galaxy—a direction in which the magnitudes are practically not

enfeebled by interstellar absorption. If these are normal stars type O—that is, giants or supergiants—and it is likely that several or even most of Zwicky's stars are of this type, we can affirm that they are largely situated outside the limits of our Galaxy. It would be sufficient if their luminosity were greater than absolute photographic magnitude $+1$ (a modest value for the luminosity of a giant and forty times that of the Sun) in order to reach this conclusion.

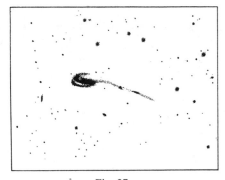

Fig. 27a
Intergalactic matter
Jet of bright material emitted from a galaxy.

2. Certain dwarf galaxies of the local cluster contain, perhaps, no more than two thousand stars, in which case the name of 'galaxy' is hardly justified. They include small clusters of stars—globular or open—much smaller than the typical globular clusters. We can, therefore, say that they are merely intergalactic stars gathered into fairly small clusters.

3. The photometer has shown the great extent of the fainter outer parts of the galaxies, and the possibility of the mingling of the outskirts of neighbouring galaxies. Further, Zwicky has drawn attention to

'arms' or 'bridges' of matter that connect galaxies that are otherwise separated from one another (although they would be considered fairly close together on the cosmic scale). Some such bridges have been known for a long time, but Zwicky and his collaborators discovered a great number of them while making a systematic search on the negatives of the sky atlas made with the 48-inch Schmidt telescope on Mount Palomar. Several surprising photographs have been published and some characteristic outlines are shown here (Fig. 27). These 'bridges' or 'cords' are, in general, multiple and complex. We have already referred to those suspected in the Magellanic Clouds.

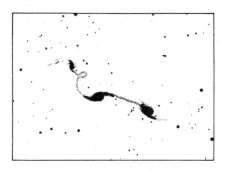

Fig. 27b
Intergalactic matter (*continued*)
Arm of material connecting three galaxies
(Paul Wild's system).

Most frequently there is a rectilineal bridge, or a simple arc, thrown out between the two galaxies by their mutual attraction, the ejected arms from each galaxy meeting and becoming united. But in accordance with tidal theory, each appendage should be accompanied by an antipodal appendage at the opposite point of the galaxy, and indeed, very often such an appendage does occur on both galaxies.

Further, the bridges are subjected to the effects of the different relative motions of the two galaxies (each having its own rotation and proper motion in space), so that we find them twisted, forming arches, spread out in plumes, or stretched out to the point of being broken. Some of these bridges are more than a million L.Y. in length. We discover them when they are luminous—that is, formed of stars. Most of them are of a blue colour, and these consist of hot stars, but ten per cent of them are reddish.

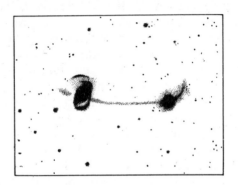

Fig. 27c
Intergalactic matter (*continued*)
Bridge between two galaxies, and antipodal jets (Keenan's system).

Zwicky estimates that a thorough examination of each of the Schmidt plates reveals an average of a dozen double or triple systems thus interwoven. If we take into consideration the possible connection by *dark* bridges, we can well believe that the existence of streams of matter between neighbouring galaxies is the general rule. The probable existence of absorb-

ing material between the Magellanic Clouds and ourselves casts suspicion on the evaluation of their distance, but this point will be hard to settle.

4. Zwicky has shown the existence of a *continuous
luminous background* in the central regions of the
large clusters of galaxies. This is undoubtedly material
scattered between the giant galaxies in these clusters.
We can imagine that it consists of escaped stars, or of
clusters escaped from large galaxies, or even of dwarf
galaxies studding the space between the large clusters.
The three kinds of objects would, in any case, be
expected to exist and to contribute to the luminous
background. We can, with confidence, add to them
gas and dust clouds. Further, in the great clusters
the occurrence of encounters frees the galaxies from
gas, which should then be found in the cluster, but
might well occur between the clusters.

5. A concrete proof of the existence of discrete
but abundant dust-clouds in the interior of the great
clusters is furnished by the statistics of galaxies.
Zwicky draws our attention to the following result,
which (according to him) is general. Let us divide a
great cluster and a rather large neighbouring area
into small squares, and count the galaxies in each
square. If we first extend the counting down to magnitude 16, then down to magnitude 18, and finally
down to magnitude 20, we obtain the surprising result
shown in Fig. 28.

Down to $m = 16$ the cluster is indicated by an
isolated peak on a background of zero density. For
$m = 18$ the central peak increases, but the density of
the galaxies in the background at a certain distance
from the peak is far from being negligible. But for
$m = 20$ we find paradoxically that the cluster is
actually *poorer* in galaxies than the sky background!

It forms a peak in the centre of a valley of negligible density, beyond which the remoter 'void' is represented by a high plateau more elevated than the peak.

The interpretation of this phenomenon is easy: a great cluster is a *dust cloud*, within which the galaxies appear much obscured in brightness. In the outskirts of the cluster the dust is such that it obliterates almost everything. At the centre, the diminution of brightness is strong, but the accumulation of galaxies is such that the impression of agglomeration persists.

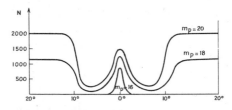

Fig. 28
Obscuration in a cluster of galaxies
Abscissae: Distance from cluster centre.
Ordinates: Number-density of galaxies.

Yet what we have considered as magnitudes 16, 18 or 20 in the centre of the 'dust bowl' undoubtedly applies to partially obscured galaxies, which are, in reality, much brighter than we perceive them. It is logical to find that the galaxies of twentieth magnitude in the remoter parts of the sky are more numerous than the galaxies of the same luminosity in the obscured zone (since the latter, being intrinsically brighter, are in reality the rarer types both in space and in the cluster).

It is probable that the *colour* of the galaxies of the cluster suffers a change, but astronomers differ in opinion on this point. Shapley's measurements—

now old—and Whitford's recent measurements negate every effect of selective intergalactic absorption (at least of one greater than the precision of the measurements), but the question should be taken up again and settled once for all. It is of the utmost importance because the presence of dust scattered in a sufficiently large amount to alter the colours would entail the presence of gas at least ten times as great in mass, quite apart from particles of large diameter. The immensity of the intergalactic domains would then oblige us to believe that the mass of diffuse matter scattered in the Universe is hundreds, or even thousands of times greater than the total mass of the galaxies. The present cosmologies would shake on their foundations if this were true.

A currently accepted number assigns to the Universe a mean density of the order of 10^{-30} gm./cm.^{3} (1 gm. of matter in 10^{30} cm.^{3}—that is, in a cube with sides of 100,000 km.). Zwicky, who has made himself the champion of a 'full' universe proposes densities ten thousand times greater (10^{-26} gm./cm.^{3}) or even more. Many astronomers (of whom I am one) consider that the mean density is at present underestimated, and that 10^{-29} or 10^{-28} are numbers which may be regarded as reasonable. But before wholeheartedly basing a cosmology on a number as high as 10^{-26} it would be advisable to make several decisive measures by proved equipment and with the most powerful means, in order to justify such a revolution.

6

Cosmology

According to the dictionary, cosmology is the science which studies the present Universe and the laws that govern it, while cosmogony is the theory of the origin of the Universe. In fact, however, the distinction is more apparent than real, for observation shows us 'young' stars (some *millions* of years old) which have been recently formed in the spiral arms of galaxies, and also 'old' stars several *thousand million* years old (let us say five thousand million years). We also see whole systems of stars on a large scale—clusters of galaxies of different ages, and the local group such as it appears today. The most distant clusters which are now available for study, are presented to our view as they were, let us say a thousand million years ago, and such a period is not negligible in the evolution of stellar systems.

The elements of duration and evolution are thus inextricably associated with our perception of the Universe. On the other hand, scientific reasoning is in no way connected with metaphysical conceptions of an absolute origin, of creation. What the scientist seeks (no matter what may be his religious or political affinities) is to understand how one state of things is caused by another, previous state. For example, he wishes to know if the galaxies have been born in the midst of a diffuse gas, or if they have originated from a medium already condensed into stars; how the spiral arms of the galaxies are formed; how the supergiants are still being born there in our own time; how the arms will disappear, etc. In other words, cosmology is henceforth inevitably involved with a more or less ambitious cosmogony. The least debatable fact is assuredly that the portion of the Universe that surrounds us is evolving, and—on a time scale of a thousand million years—at a very great speed.

Some stars are born, some explode, some pulsate; all are consumed in radiating light and particles. Some stellar associations develop before our eyes, others are broken up at a known rhythm; the rotation of the galaxies dissociates local stellar groups and mixes their materials. The galaxies themselves are deformed and broken up by the effect of neighbouring ones; they collide and interpenetrate in the clusters, where they describe immense orbits. These clusters themselves are associated and evolve conjointly, and in the meantime the entire Universe, according to all appearances, expands and disperses its matter with great speed. But all these factors have been brought to our knowledge or attention only in the last two decades or so. The earlier conception of the Universe was based rather on the slowness of its evolution— but that was already an immense advance on the immutability dear to the Ancients.

We need not, however, be astonished if even an innovator like Einstein began by elaborating a *static* model of the Universe (1918). But before we can discuss this the very idea of a 'cosmological model' requires some explanation.

A few words of history. It is well known that some pioneers in the second half of the 18th century already considered that the Galaxy was a cosmic unit on a large scale and conjectured that certain nebulae, pale and amorphous in appearance, were other distant and unresolved galaxies. Naturally no proof of this was given.

But in the 19th century stellar astronomy went ahead with such strides that speculative constructions seem to have thereby suffered. Some readily imagined an infinite space peopled with stars in an almost uniform way, the Milky Way being only a region fortuitously overpopulated. Others identified the Galaxy with the Universe and supposed that *nothing* exists outside it. In 1920 such conceptions still defied in heated controversy the conceptions established today, of a universe populated by galaxies, or rather by clusters of galaxies, to be precise.

The general theory of relativity and cosmology. When Einstein had established his law of gravitation its success in the prediction of local phenomena was striking. In the solar system, or in the vicinity of neighbouring stars, it had been shown that there was evidence for:

(*a*) The deviation of light by material masses.

(*b*) An additional motion of the perihelia of orbits.

(*c*) A slowing down of clocks (atomic vibrations) by gravitational fields.

But these new properties imply a deformation of space by the presence of matter; space thus loses its metaphysical existence as independent of matter, and is identified with the region where the gravitational field and the electro-magnetic field allow those measurements that characterise and define the properties of space itself. Space becomes a *physical* quantity.

But the continuum thus established no longer presents the characteristics of classical geometry, called Euclidean. Space is said to be *curved*, but this adjective is doubtless more detrimental than useful, for though we can correctly picture a sheet of cardboard (two dimensions) being bent in a-space of three dimensions, we cannot at all imagine a space of three dimensions being bent in a domain possessing a fourth dimension. This mental gymnastics is futile; we are unable to conceive (except in the symbolism of mathematics) of a fourth dimension of *space*; and, in fact, relativistic space has only three dimensions. Its *curvature* is represented in a simple algebraic manner: our measures of length no longer behave according to the rules of ordinary geometry; Pythagoras's theorem, for example, no longer applies.

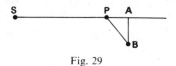

Fig. 29

Let us imagine a small radial displacement PA (Fig. 29) with reference to the Sun, followed by a transverse displacement AB at right angles to PA. No longer have we $PB^2 = PA^2 + AB^2$, as in Euclidean space. We have

$$PB^2 = \frac{PA^2}{K} + AB^2 \tag{1}$$

K being a factor which depends on the mass of the Sun and the distance SP. (K is slightly less than 1). The radial distance PA is equivalent to

$$\frac{PA}{\sqrt{K}}$$

if we wish to interpret the relation (1) in Euclidean lengths and to recover the Pythagorean combination.

The *radial* lengths are increased, the transverse lengths are unaltered. From this it follows that the ratio of the circumference of a circle to its diameter is diminished in the geometry of the neighbourhood of P. Some value of π less than that with which we are familiar is appropriate for measurements close to P.

In fact, if we take no notice of very small displacements which could be identified with segments of straight lines, the physical geometry of the space around the masses of matter represented by the stars excludes the existence of straight lines. There are no straight lines in *actual* space, any more than on the surface of a sphere or any other curved surface. Having admitted this, the question of the *shape* of the Universe, considered as a whole, arises in the same way as the question of the shape of the Earth was presented to the Ancients.

It is well known that, in spite of mountains and valleys, man commenced by imagining the Earth, taken as a whole, as *flat*. The flat appearance of the vast sea, or of very extensive deserts, led him to regard local humps and depressions as of relatively small importance. But then observation of far away objects on the sea, and the long voyages which showed progressive changes of the constellations in the sky, led to the view of a regular *curvature* of the surface of the ground, independent of local relief and of a much more fundamental nature. The curvature could be imagined by ignoring small local deformations; and if the Earth's surface is curved, where does this curvature lead? Could it not be that the surface closes in on itself and that the Earth is a ball? It remained for this elaborate conception to be verified by astronomical observations (by the shape of the Earth's shadow, for instance, during eclipses of the

Moon), and then to measure the Earth by evaluating its constant curvature. This is what Eratosthenes did iu the third century B.C. These fine results were thus acquired nearly 2,000 years before man was able to circumnavigate his planet.

The cosmological problem. The problem of the overall shape, of the geometrical structure of the Universe, is presented, as we have said, in an analogous manner. We are certain that matter is capable of altering the properties of *physical* space, or rather of altering the false idea of ideal space that we made for ourselves. In the neighbourhood of the Sun space is not Euclidean—no one can any longer doubt this. From region to region around the stars we shall find, therefore, various curvatures, appropriate to their different masses and their degree of concentration of matter. But if we leave aside these local bumps, is there not a general curvature of the Universe? Is the total matter that studs the Universe able to affect the Universe as a whole in the same manner in which each hump causes its local effects? What reason should we have for desiring, *a priori*, a Euclidean and infinite Universe, when we have established that at least it is not Euclidean around each star?

Undoubtedly the Universe has a general structure less simple than the Euclidean and necessarily infinite picture which science unreservedly attributed to it when non-Euclidean geometries did not exist. The doubt once born, it was necessary to pose the problem, to consider theoretically all possible solutions, and then to try to see, by observation, to which of these solutions the Universe appears to conform.

*Einstein's solution.** Some simplifying conventions

---

*For further details see *The Expansion of the Universe*, translated by J. B. Sidgwick (Faber, 1952).

had to be introduced by Einstein to eliminate the local humps. He supposed that the matter of the stars is dispersed in space and that it is uniformly distributed. In other words, the Universe was treated as if it were a gaseous haze of constant density. Einstein then asked what system of measurement, what geometry, would prevail in such a Universe if the laws of general relativity are presumed to apply?

Struck by the smallness of stellar speeds in comparison with the speed of light (for the apparent speeds of recession of the distant galaxies were unknown at that time), Einstein supposed that the mean degree of agitation of his haze was zero, and sought for a *static* solution—that is, a system of measurement independent of time, which means a stable model. Luckily, the homogeneous isotropic spaces suitable to the relativistic laws of gravitation are not numerous. Only three of them exist: *Euclidean* space (which, with its zero curvature, appears immediately to the physicist as a highly improbable special case), *Lobatchevsky's* space (which is the picture provided by the first non-Euclidean geometry devised in the last century), and finally, *spherical* space with a constant positive curvature—that is, closed on itself. (Its form is the boundary of a hypersphere, familiar to mathematicians but not simple to describe to the layman, who may, however, be informed that the radius R is not to be conceived as a simple 'length'.)

In 1917, Einstein showed that only the third space fitted the problem that he had posed, and he published the formulae of a static model in which the only unknown factor was the density ρ of the haze. It was necessary to ascertain a value for this from observation. The radius R of the hypersphere and the total mass M of the Universe are simply expressed as functions of ρ. But the value of ρ is still highly controversial—as we have seen—and the interest of Einstein's results becomes less clear if the hypothesis of a stable and static model is not valid.

De Sitter's Empty Universe. Already in 1917, the Dutch astronomer, de Sitter, showed that another solution would be possible if we imagined $\rho = 0$. This proposal seems futile; we have established the existence of stars, of clusters of stars, and of galaxies; therefore ρ is not zero. De Sitter's model, however, appears as an *asymptotic* solution—that is, a model towards which a Universe in expansion would *tend* to develop as it grew larger and its density diminished. Further, this model appeared as the setting for *systematic movements*: if we introduce into the empty model *one* observer and *one* particle, the observer will see the particle running away.

Finally, whereas Einstein's Universe is *full* (as far as it can be, since it is in equilibrium) but *static*, de Sitter's Universe is *empty* but endowed with the appearance of recession for distant objects.

THE EXPANDING UNIVERSE

A strange dilemma was presented to astronomers when observation of the galaxies showed appearances of universal recession. The real Universe behaved as regards matter in accordance with Einstein's Universe, but as regards systematic motions in accordance with de Sitter's Universe. Which should be chosen? How could the two solutions be reconciled?

In 1922, the mathematician A. Friedmann discovered that the cosmological problem was capable of an infinity of solutions if we abandoned the hypothesis of a static Universe (which had been tacitly implied). In other words, if we allow the system of measurement to vary as a function of the time, models conformable to general relativity can be either *closed* but with a variable radius (passing in time from Einstein's model to de Sitter's model), or infinite and *open*, but with constant alteration of the mutal distances of the objects.

In addition, the probability of a non-static Universe increased when Eddington showed that Einstein's static and occupied Universe would be in unstable equilibrium. It would be static only in a precarious manner, like a house of cards; the least internal disturbance would destroy the equilibrium. The discovery that the Universe appears to be in disequilibrium was thus shown to conform with the most abstruse theoretical researches. This agreement between observation and theory seems at the present time to be a good omen both for the theory and for a sound interpretation of the facts.

WHAT MODEL SHOULD WE CHOOSE?

At a time when the observation of galaxies was still precarious, and when theoretical researches were held to be suspect (and sometimes ignored), the Abbé George Lemaître put forward in 1927 a model in which theory and observation were simultaneously considered and brought into agreement. This was doubtless the best synthesis that could then be proposed. Lemaître accepted as a starting point Einstein's static model and considered the present Universe as a phase of its expansion. Reconstructing his work later, Lemaître no longer considered the static state as transitory. According to him, the Universe, starting in a condition of extreme density (that is, from the famous 'primitive atom'), exploded, expanded, and passed slowly through Einstein's stage of unstable equilibrium; it has continued to expand on its original impetus ever since.

There have been many theories following the Lemaître model, but there is one of recent interest which, though based on the idea of expansion, is substantially difficient. This is the 'Steady State' hypothesis of H. Bondi and T. Gold, as developed and popularized by Fred Hoyle. This theory denies that the expansion results from an 'explosion' of a superdense primordial cosmic 'atom'. It explains the expansion as a continual making-room for newly-created atoms of hydrogen in intergalactic space. These atoms are presumed to arrive inconspicuously, one here and one there, and to have no origin in terms of known physical processes. The present size of the Universe is so great that the new matter must come in at the rate of 10^{32} tons of hydrogen per second. The Universe expands at a rate that exactly makes room for it, and so its density remains steady. On this hypothesis, the Universe was no denser six thousand million years ago than it is today.*

It has been suggested that evidence as to whether the Steady State hypothesis is to be given credence or not may be obtained in the future by extremely powerful radio-telescopes, capable of detecting objects whose speed of recession is close to that of light. If the Universe in some sense 'began' six thousand million years ago, such objects would be observed as they were comparatively soon after they were formed, and only a small proportion of them would show the characteristics of maturity. But if a fair sample of them is found to differ in no way from the objects at present under observation, then they will provide evidence in favour of a steady state hypothesis. There is no generally accepted evidence at present.*

At present it still appears difficult to choose between the Lemaître model and the many others which have since been proposed. We have seen the changes in the measurement of distances; the measurement of the masses of the galaxies is just beginning; intergalactic matter has been discovered. He would be truly presumptuous—or even frivolous, I think—who professed to know within a factor of 100 the value of the mean density ρ of the realm explored up to the present! But it is this value ρ which, associated with the value of the recession, will allow us to say whether the Universe is open or closed, and, if it is closed, what is its radius. It is equally plausible that more complex, non-homogeneous models, will modify the very nature of the question.

Any precision on the structure of the Universe seems now to be impossible, in spite of recent advances in exploration—we might even say, because of them. We seem less confident than we were ten years ago that we are confronted with a relatively simple problem.

VALIDITY OF THE THEORY OF THE EXPANSION OF THE UNIVERSE

The discovery of the instability of the relativistic *models* of the Universe, implying *a priori* that there must be either expansion or contraction, and, on the other hand, the subsequent discovery of an apparent recession of all distant objects, have given a very high degree of probability to the expansion of the Universe. The very rapid evolution of the Universe and the ages of the various heavenly bodies also

*Translator's addition (both paragraphs).

argue in favour of expansion.

Certain astronomers appeal to a peculiar argument against expansion: the theory is supposedly unfounded because it is deduced from a *model* of the Universe; the conclusions are considered to be a property of a model and of the model only—not of the real Universe.

A *model* is a simplified representation of the complexity of the real Universe. We may, therefore, ask these sceptics whether they know of any single scientific 'law' which is not the expression of a model, of a schematised representation of reality?

Mankind will never create more than an approximate representation of the Universe, and models will always be used in the natural sciences everywhere and in every field. In my view, this objection is completely without foundation.

THE AGE OF THE UNIVERSE

The expansion of the Universe depends, before everything else, on observation and on general relativity. But the interpretation of the observed red shift in terms of a recession is rendered very plausible by a remarkable agreement in the times involved. We have seen that the recession corresponds to a speed of 55 km./sec. per million L.Y. of distance. A vehicle moving uniformly at this speed would take 6,000 million years to traverse a million L.Y. In other words, if the recession is real and has taken place uniformly, the galaxies were practically in contact with one another 6,000 million years ago. The Universe would have passed through a stage of congestion, with minimum radius. This single block-Universe was named the '*primitive* atom' by the Abbé Lemaître, who sees in it a real 'beginning'. The present Universe would have proceeded from this primitive state by explosion, by a kind of radio-active disintegration of this atom.

In no way do I approve of the metaphysical commentaries with which this postulated hyperdense state of the Universe has been accompanied. Some have pointed to it as a vindication of the 'creation' of the world; others have condemned it for the same reason, or because of its association with Einstein's Relativity—or again because it is said to be a 'bourgeois' theory. I see nothing at all in these extravagances and am persuaded that science will discover a rational explanation for it. Moreover, already many models (whether 'oscillating' or not) explain it as a '*bottle-neck*' passage from a phase of contraction to a phase of expansion.

But it seems to me that a more urgent need for astronomers than discussions on the exact condition of the point singularity is to settle the question whether the Doppler displacement really implies a recession. It is true that all theories adverse to the recession for the last thirty years have foundered, one after the other, but some new property of light may one day be discovered and give an immediate explanation of the phenomenon. In the meantime, figure of six thousand million years seems to be very significant and to provide a strong argument in favour of the recession. The old figure, prior to its increase by the correction factors, was on the contrary an argument *against* recession, for it implied an age less than that of the Earth itself. It is, then, fair to consider the rectified number as an argument for the recession, particularly as it fits in with other temporal data that we possess.

We should carefully note that the Universe has

not necessarily evolved at a uniform speed. We can imagine delays a little longer, or a little shorter, by supposing that the process is retarded or accelerated. It remains nonetheless true that the figure of six thousand million years is *characteristic* in the theory of expansion. If we evoke the age of the globular clusters (about five thousand million years), and the Earth's age (four thousand million years), we must acknowledge that evolution appears to be under happy auspices. Besides, a Universe that is static, or in a stationary state, could not be said to have *any* age.

But one would be blind to deny the abundant signs of rapid evolution that we see around us. The stars use up their hydrogen, the galaxies rotate and mingle their clouds, and they intercollide in the clusters. Expansion does nothing but assist these processes. The fact that the typical spectral red shift does not occur in the heart of the local cluster supplies further reason for believing that the shift really does correspond to a recession.

To sum up, pending a proof to the contrary, the expansion of the Universe has all the appearance of a valid and substantial theory.

The (P,P) Cycle

$$H^1 + H^1 = H^2 + \text{positron} + \text{neutrino} \nearrow \qquad (1)$$
$$H^2 + H^1 = He^3 \qquad\qquad + \text{energy} \qquad (2)$$
$$He^3 + He^3 = He^4 + 2H^1 \qquad (3)$$

Reaction (2) is almost instantaneous. Reaction (1) is slow. Each formation of helium, He^4, corresponds to the effective liberation of about 4.10^{-5} erg.

The (C,N) Cycle

$$C^{12} + H^1 = N^{13} + \text{energy} \qquad (1)$$
$$N^{13} = C^{13} + \text{positron} + \text{neutrino} \nearrow$$
$$C^{13} + H^1 = N^{14} + \text{energy} \qquad (2)$$
$$N^{14} + H^1 = O^{15} + \text{energy} \qquad (3)$$
$$O^{15} = N^{15} + \text{positron} + \text{neutrino} \nearrow$$
$$N^{15} + H^1 = C^{12} + He^4 \qquad (4)$$

In the two cycles, the neutrinos escape without contributing to the heat or light of the star.

In the (C,N) cycle the liberated and useful energy is a little less than in the (P,P) cycle because of the second neutrino, which escapes, but it remains little less than 4.10^{-5} erg per He^4 nucleus formed.

Reaction (3) seems the slowest, but we are still doubtful about its speed. If it is not reaction (3), it is reaction (1) which, by its slowness, would check the cycle.

APPENDIX II

Age T of the Terrestial Crust

Let u be the number of original atoms of uranium 238 in a given region, as deduced from the relative proportion of lead 204. Then at the end of time t, we have by definition a remaining amount λu. $e^{-\lambda_1 t}$ (λ_1 being the well-known radioactive constant of U 238). The number of atoms of Pb 206 generated during this time is u $(1 - e^{-\lambda_1 t})$, and the ratio between the masses of the lead generated and the residual uranium will be

$$\frac{206}{238} \left(\frac{1 - e^{-\lambda_1 t}}{e^{-\lambda_1 t}} \right)$$

This being so, if x is the initial amount of Pb 206, and x_m its amount at the past epoch t_m (the time being reckoned backwards from the present epoch), we have:

$$x_m = x + u \left[1 - e^{-\lambda_1 (T - t_m)} \right] \tag{1}$$

Similarly, with Pb 207 and U 235 we have:

$$y_m = y + v \left[1 - e^{-\lambda_2 (T - t_m)} \right] \tag{2}$$

(y and y_m being the amounts of Pb 207, v the initial amount of U 235, and λ_2 the constant for U 235).

The ratio U 238/U 235 is at present 139; therefore, in accordance with the original definition, we have:

$$\frac{u}{v} = 139 \, \frac{e^{\lambda_1 T}}{e^{\lambda_1 T}} \tag{3}$$

Eliminating u and v from the three preceding equations, we find that:

$$\frac{x_m - x}{y_m - y} = 139 \, \frac{e^{\lambda_1 T} - e^{\lambda_1 t_m}}{e^{\lambda_2 T} - e^{\lambda_2 t_m}} \tag{4}$$

(T, x, y are the unknowns, t_m, x_m, y_m are given by analyses, λ_1, λ_2 are given by laboratory measurements).

Three samples of mineral, dated and analysed, are sufficient to provide three equations like (4) and to determine the three unknowns. The best solution for a large number of samples is obtained by the method of least squares.

INDEX

127